Connect to
NCTM Standards 2000

Making the Standards
Work at Grade 5

Francis (Skip) Fennell, Ph.D.

Honi J. Bamberger, Ph.D.

Thomas E. Rowan, Ph.D.

Kay B. Sammons

Anna R. Suarez

Creative Publications
A Tribune Education Company

Acknowledgments

Project Editors → Diane Nieker, Jeff Stiegel

Writers → Tim Burnett, Marilyn Davis, Beth Sycamore

Writing and Editorial Services → MathLink, Inc.

Design Director → Karen Stack

Design → Gerta Sorensen-London

Project Coordinator → Barbara Quincer

Cover Illustration → Jim Dandy

Illustrators → Susan Aiello, Jim Dandy, Sarah Frederking

Production → Graphic Advantage, Ltd.

Manufacturing → Dallas Richards

© 2000 Creative Publications®, Inc.
Two Prudential Plaza
Chicago, IL 60601

This is an independent publication and is not affiliated with, or sponsored by, the NCTM. The NCTM 2000 Standards are not reproduced in this book. This book is designed to be read independently of the *Principles and Standards for School Mathematics* and to aid educators in preparing to teach in a manner consistent with the *Principles and Standards.*

ISBN 0-7622-1247-0
Catalog No. 21508
Customer Service 800-624-0822
http://www.creativepublications.com
1 2 3 4 5 6 7 8 MAL 05 04 03 02 01 00

Contents

Overview

Since *Curriculum and Evaluation Standards for School Mathematics* was released in 1989, much has been learned about how ideas work in the classroom and how students learn mathematics. The release of the *Principles and Standards for School Mathematics* creates an opportunity for us to examine our goals, our math curricula, and our teaching methods in light of these new insights and to consider practices and procedures that will improve school mathematics education. As did the original draft, *Principles and Standards* promotes ways for all educators to strengthen the teaching and learning of mathematics by addressing two important concerns: the characteristics of instructional programs that will provide high-quality mathematical experiences for students as they progress through school, and the mathematical content and processes students should know and use as they advance from grade to grade.

General Overview

Connect to NCTM Standards 2000 is designed to help you understand and implement the NCTM standards. Regardless of your teaching style, the information presented in this book will help you to make the standards work. *Principles and Standards* identifies ten standards. Five of those standards are described as content standards that organize all of mathematics into five broad areas of learning; they address *what* students learn. The other five standards, the process standards, are concerned with *how* students learn and how information is presented.

Today, more than ever, there is a need for all students to have a strong base in mathematics. This means that students do not just memorize facts and procedures, but that they have an understanding of mathematics and mathematical thinking. The interplay between content and process is complicated, but integrating the two is critical if our students are to receive the mathematics education they will need to function effectively in the world they will grow into.

The lessons contained within *Connect to NCTM Standards 2000* are organized into sections by content. Each section contains four lessons dealing with some aspect of that content standard. Each lesson demonstrates ways to develop the content by using the process standards. An overview highlights grade-level content skills and gives a brief description of the four lessons for that standard.

Content Standards

Number and Operation

Algebra

Geometry

Measurement

Data Analysis and Probability

Process Standards

Problem Solving

Reasoning and Proof

Communication

Connections

Representation

The last section of the book, entitled Create Your Own Lesson, is designed to help you develop lessons of your own that will comfortably incorporate the NCTM standards with your teaching style.

About the Lessons

Each content standard section contains four lessons that address some aspect of the content at the grade level. Three of the lessons have been specially developed to model ways the process standards can be used to develop the content being presented. The fourth lesson examines a hypothetical math textbook lesson in terms of how the process standards are incorporated into that lesson. Suggestions are offered for increasing the focus on three of the five process standards to create a more effective lesson. Then, a lesson is presented modeling how those suggestions can be implemented.

As you read through the lessons, keep in mind that what is offered is only one possible approach. You might have a completely different idea about how to develop the concept, and that's fine. These lessons are intended to provide examples of how the process standards can work to make mathematics lessons more meaningful, and to model questions and techniques that you might incorporate into your teaching. As you read through the lessons, pay attention to how the process standards are being used. Use the ideas presented as a springboard for your own ideas.

Each lesson is intended for a single class period. Some introduce a concept, others require that students have some experience with the concept, and still others are meant to be used at the end of a unit. As you examine these lessons, think about how and where they fit into your curriculum. Any of the lessons here can be used as a replacement for the comparable lesson in your current math program. Try the lessons and see the difference incorporating the process standards can make.

Creating Your Own Lessons

The last section of the book is designed to help you develop lessons of your own that incorporate the NCTM standards and are compatible with your teaching style. You will find questions to help you focus on ideas to consider as you begin to organize a standards-based lesson. You will also have an opportunity to follow the thoughts and decisions one person used in the process of developing a lesson.

About the Authors

Francis (Skip) Fennell, Ph.D.

Dr. Fennell was a member of the writing team of *Principles and Standards for School Mathematics* (NCTM, 2000). He has authored mathematics textbooks, materials for both students and teachers, and numerous articles for leading mathematics journals. Dr. Fennell has served on the Board of Directors of NCTM and as Program Officer of instructional materials and teacher enhancement within the Division of Elementary, Secondary, and Informal Education at the National Science Foundation. He has been selected as Outstanding Mathematics Educator by the Maryland Council of Teachers of Mathematics, and as Professor of the Year by both the Carnegie Foundation and Western Maryland College, where he is a professor of education.

Honi J. Bamberger, Ph.D.

Dr. Bamberger is a recognized math scholar and teacher. She has taught at both the elementary school and college levels, served as an associate research scientist and mathematics consultant for Johns Hopkins University, and contributed as a consultant and content writer for the "Numbers Alive" public television series. Dr. Bamberger has presented her research findings at mathematics conferences across the country, and has been an author for a number of mathematics textbooks. Currently, Dr. Bamberger is executive director of Insight, a consulting firm specializing in professional development in mathematics education.

Thomas E. Rowan, Ph.D.

Dr. Rowan was a member of the working group that wrote the K–4 section of the *Curriculum and Evaluation Standards for School Mathematics*. Since the Standards were first published, he has worked with many school systems to help bring about the transition to standards-based classroom mathematics instruction in grades K–8. Dr. Rowan is a frequent presenter at NCTM and author of mathematics texts and numerous articles on teaching and learning mathematics. He currently teaches at the University of Maryland where he focuses on methods of teaching elementary school mathematics.

Kay B. Sammons

Kay Sammons is currently Elementary Mathematics Supervisor for the Howard County Public Schools in Ellicott City, Maryland, where she is responsible for curriculum and staff development for elementary teachers. She is a frequent presenter at state and national mathematics conferences. In addition to serving as a reviewer for NCTM publications, she has written textbooks and teacher resource materials. Ms. Sammons was honored as Elementary Mathematics Teacher of the Year by the Maryland Council Teachers of Mathematics and as Outstanding Educator of the Year by that same organization.

Anna R. Suarez

Anna Suarez is a national consultant and program director for K–8 Mathematics at the National Science Foundation in Arlington, Virginia. Her participation in an NSF-funded research study, Cognitively Guided Instruction (C.G.I.), helped to develop teachers' knowledge of students' mathematical thinking as the basis for making instructional decisions. She has written staff development materials for both the *Investigations* curriculum and Insight.

About the Standards

The *Principles and Standards for School Mathematics 2000* are built around ten curriculum standards. Five of those standards address the mathematical content, or body of mathematical knowledge, that students should learn. Content standards prescribe *what* is to be taught in mathematics. The content standards are Number and Operation, Algebra, Geometry, Measurement, and Data Analysis and Probability.

The other five standards are process standards. The process standards describe *how* the content is delivered. They address how students will acquire the necessary mathematical content and how that knowledge will be applied. The five process standards are identified as Problem Solving, Reasoning and Proof, Communication, Connections, and Representation.

It should be pointed out that the content standards and process standards are not separate subsets of the whole, but are intricately interrelated. How mathematics is learned is as important as what mathematics is learned. The process standards help to "frame" how the content standards are presented.

It is possible to weave the process standards into the teaching of mathematics through a variety of methods. Students can and should be presented with meaningful problems to solve and situations that require them to reason through information to find solutions. They should be asked to defend their solutions and explain their thinking. In presenting a problem to students, connections might be made to a similar problem to build on previous learning. A representative model might be used to enhance students' understanding of a concept. Continuous communication, written and oral, will provide feedback about students' understanding.

For students to become mathematically powerful, it is essential that they be able to use process skills flexibly. They need to practice applying reasoning to solve problems and proving that their solutions are correct. They need to experiment with a variety of representations and have the ability to use them in solving problems and in illustrating their thinking. They should be able to communicate their mathematical thinking and solutions to the teacher and to other students both orally and in writing. Making connections between problems within mathematics is as essential as is making mathematical connections to disciplines outside of mathematics. The importance of how these processes interrelate and work together cannot be overemphasized.

Content Standards

Number and Operation

Algebra

Geometry

Measurement

Data Analysis and Probability

Process Standards

Problem Solving

Reasoning and Proof

Communication

Connections

Representation

Intermediate Problem Solving

PROBLEM SOLVING IS AT THE HEART of mathematics—it is what mathematicians do. Balance is achieved through the interrelationship of conceptual learning, basic skills, and problem solving. Students need to develop concepts with concrete representations to ensure understanding and to build a strong foundation. They need basic skills in order to apply their understandings with efficiency. But most importantly, they need good problems to solve, problems in which they can apply their conceptual understandings and utilize basic skills.

In its simplest form, problem solving means finding a solution when the answer is not readily apparent. Because problem solving does not always follow a uniform plan, students need to develop persistence to be able to work problems through to the end. Sometimes persistence means changing direction. *Well, we know that way doesn't work. What should we try next? Is there another way we can look at this problem?* Questions that encourage students to look for other options should be an integral part of the discussions that take place in mathematics classes.

Choosing problems that have relevance to students is an important factor in creating enthusiasm for problem solving. Often, the enthusiasm of the teacher translates into a positive disposition toward problem solving to students. If statements like, "Now that's an unusual problem. I wonder how we can find the answer," are part of a teacher's repertoire, children get the notion that problem solving is interesting and they are encouraged to use their own resources to find a path to the solution.

Acquiring a variety of strategies to access for problem solving is essential to experiencing success. Having flexibility to solve problems in different ways enables students to get "unstuck" if they reach a "dead end." It allows them to have other approaches to try. Students should be provided with instruction and practice in using a wide range of strategies to draw upon.

When intermediate grade students are presented with a problem which doesn't exactly conform to what has been learned previously, they need to develop strategies based on their skills and concepts.

A fourth grade teacher presented the following problem to the class:

How many different rectangles can you find on your geoboard?
Work with a partner and record your solutions on geoboard dot paper.

Interesting communication ensued between students and teacher from the beginning of the lesson. *What is a rectangle?*

Scott responded, "A shape with four corners."

What is the word that mathematicians use to describe corners?

"They're angles," suggested Kiesha.

What do we know about the angles of a rectangle?

"They are all right angles," Armando stated.

Does anyone know how many degrees are in a right angle?

"Ninety degrees," contributed Ryan.

Show me a rectangle on your geoboard.

The students used their rubber bands to make rectangles on their geoboards. The teacher held up Kristen's geoboard. *What do you think about the shape Kristen found?*

"That's a square, not a rectangle," offered Anna.

"But a square is a rectangle," argued Kristen.

Following a discussion about the properties of rectangles and squares, the students were paired to begin their exploration. The teacher described the parameters of the problem. *Your task today is to find all the different rectangles you can on your geoboard. The rectangles must all be different. If the rectangle is just in a different place or flipped on its side, it doesn't count as being different.*

As the students were discovering and recording their "finds," the teacher checked to make sure there were no duplicates and prompted students to think of ways to create rectangles. *I wonder if you could find a rectangle that is tilted. Would that be different than the straight ones? Can you find a rectangle that is similar to this one, but a little larger?*

After students had found several rectangles, a class discussion was held for students to share their findings. Using an overhead model of a geoboard, different students demonstrated rectangles they had found. As each rectangle was identified, pairs tried to find the same one on their geoboard dot paper. If they were unable to find it, they were directed to construct it on their geoboard and record it on their geoboard dot paper. By the end of the math period, the class had found 15 different rectangles. The teacher let them know that they had done a wonderful job and then closed the lesson with a challenge. *There are 16 possible rectangles. Do you think someone will be able to find the 16th rectangle?*

This engaging problem-solving activity provides an example of how the processes work together in a lesson. Connections were made as students clarified definitions and represented shapes with geoboards and drawings. Communication was woven into all parts of the lesson from the introductory dialogue with the class through the questions posed to students during the exploration to the culminating discussion. Reasoning and proof was involved in identifying and proving that rectangles were different from one another.

Problem solving should be at the core of any mathematics curriculum. Through working well-chosen problems, students are challenged to apply the skills they have learned in new ways that expand their thinking and understanding of concepts. Students who are consistently presented with challenging problems learn to develop and apply new strategies. When they are also given opportunities to communicate their strategies with others and reflect on their thinking, their problem solving abilities are further enhanced.

Intermediate Reasoning and Proof

REASONING IS FUNDAMENTAL TO THE STUDY of mathematics— it is a state of mind that causes students to explore, to justify, and to validate. It permeates all content areas and all grade levels. Students are reasoning when they interpret data, when they solve problems, and when they view geometric patterns and shapes. As they are presented with new problems, they use reasoning skills to apply previously acquired information and to test the validity of their solutions. Reasoning is the process by which students make sense of mathematics.

As they develop mathematically, students learn that mathematics is a discipline based on an inherent set of rules. Reasoning begins with intuition. This intuition is used by the even the youngest children in their efforts to make sense of mathematics, and it should be encouraged as the basis of reasoning at all grade levels. This informal intuition will become the basis for reasoning through representations that are more formal and for proofs based upon the rules.

What are some ways reasoning and proof can be incorporated into the mathematics class? An excellent way is to ask questions that hold students accountable for their thinking. *How did you get your answer? Tell me how you thought about that. Why does your solution work? Do you think that strategy will always work?*

Piaget believed that for children to develop reasoning, it was imperative to have social interaction. A powerful means of achieving this interaction is through mathematical discussions. Designating time during the class for students to put forth their ideas for examination is critical. Students must learn to explain and defend their thinking. They must also learn to detect unsound reasoning in explanations presented by other students. In any given class there will be a wide range of reasoning abilities. It is helpful for students with less mature reasoning to hear from those with well-developed skills. These mathematical discussions increase a student's repertoire of reasoning skills.

What do these mathematical discussions look like? A teacher typically presents a problem to the class that may be related to concepts being studied. Early in the year, before the multiplication algorithm was introduced, the following problem was presented to a fourth grade class.

What is 24 × 6?

After time was allowed for students to solve the problem, they were asked to share their responses.

- The first student reported that the answer was 144.
  When asked by the teacher to explain how he got the answer he said, "I multiplied 20 times 6 and got 120. Then I multiplied 4 × 6 and got 24. I added 120 and 24 and got 144."

- Another student responded, "I got 144 too, but I did it differently." When asked to explain how she got the answer, she responded, "I thought that 24 is close to 25 and 25 is like a quarter. So I thought of 6 quarters and that would be $1.50. But that is too much because there are only 24 and not 25 so I had to subtract 6 from $1.50. I got 144."

- A third student interjected, "I got 144 too, but I did it a different way. I broke 24 into 10 + 10 + 4 because it's easier for me to multiply tens. I multiplied 10 × 6 and got 60. I had to do it twice. I got 120. Then I multiplied the 6 times the 4 and got 24. I added it to the 120 and got 144."

The teacher asked if this third solution was related in any way to the others. One student said, "It's a lot like the first one, but instead of multiplying 20 × 6, 10 was multiplied by 6 and then doubled." Whether a student is explaining his answer to the class or listening to the explanation of another, the time spent on this kind of discussion is invaluable. All students benefit when they are asked to defend their answers as well as to reflect on someone else's solution to determine whether it makes sense.

Intermediate Communication

WHETHER BETWEEN TEACHER AND STUDENT, between a pair of students, or among groups of students, the communication skills of reading, writing, listening, and speaking provide the means for sharing ideas and promoting mathematical understanding. As students express their ideas through oral and written language, they have an opportunity to clarify their thinking and reinforce their own comprehension of the concepts they are working with. By listening to explanations given by their classmates, students are exposed to ideas they may not have thought of. This provides a greater network of connections among ideas and, in turn, enhances learning.

Ample opportunities to discuss mathematical ideas should be provided. One way to promote this is to present an interesting problem to the class, allow time to solve the problem, and then ask students to explain how they solved the problem. Providing a forum for a number of different solutions to be presented and defended by students results in rich dialogue. There is a very high level of mental activity associated with social interactions of this nature. Students who are afforded opportunities to take part in these mathematical conversations on a regular basis learn more effectively how to reason and defend their answers. In the process, they also learn to communicate and to clarify and refine their ideas, which leads to deeper understanding.

When students are able to communicate their ideas, the teacher is provided with insight into their thinking. As an example, the following problem might be given to students.

> **A minivan can seat 6 students plus the driver.** *How many minivans will be needed to transport a class of 32 students on a field trip?*

Students will solve this problem in a variety of ways.

- They might draw rectangles to represent buses and put 6 tally marks in each rectangle to stand for the number of students each van will hold.
- Some might count by sixes.
- Students might apply the division algorithm to this problem—getting an answer of 5 remainder 2.

This last solution prompts an interesting discussion. *What does a remainder of 2 really mean in this problem? Can you have 2 students left over? Does a remainder make sense in this situation?* Going back to the question of how many minivans will be needed all together helps clarify the answer. Because the students have had additional time to review and reflect on the problem, their understanding is enhanced.

Putting ideas on paper is another means of helping students organize their thinking. Writing causes a student to reflect on ideas and refine them before committing that thinking to paper. Often, at the end of a lesson, students will be asked to communicate what they learned in the problem or investigation they just completed. This reflection can be an important tool for teachers in assessing their students' understanding. Words, pictures, numbers and symbols are all important parts of written communication that students have at their disposal, and students are becoming much more adept at using mathematical symbols to communicate their thinking. Many teachers use journal writing as a way for students to relate what they know about mathematics.

Intermediate students should be provided with regular opportunities to use both oral and written language and to share mathematical ideas with their teachers and peers on a daily basis.

Intermediate Connections

MAKING CONNECTIONS IN MATHEMATICS is a three-fold process. First, connections are made when one mathematical idea is used to build another. Second, connections are made among different mathematical ideas. Third, connections are made between mathematics and contexts outside the field of mathematics.

Because mathematics is an integrated discipline, treating it as a whole body of knowledge and focusing on the connections that occur naturally adds dimension to ideas and concepts. How is counting related to addition, addition to subtraction, addition to multiplication, multiplication to area? A cohesive curriculum that is clearly articulated from pre-kindergarten through the twelfth grade, one that connects the mathematical ideas within each grade as well as the mathematics between grade levels, is critical if those connections are to take place.

Making connections to prior mathematical experiences is vital for the understanding of how mathematical ideas build on one another. Teachers need to know what mathematics students learned previously in order to build on that knowledge. In a given unit of study, attention should be paid to ensure that mathematics concepts build upon one another from day to day in a coherent manner. Teachers should also be aware of what their students will be studying in subsequent grades so they can lay the foundation for obvious connections to further studies.

Mathematics permeates other subject areas as well as the physical world of students. The use of shapes and patterns is prevalent in art and architecture; measurement skills and classification skills are important in science; measurement skills and knowledge of fractions are utilized in cooking and building models; and measurement skills and data gathering and statistics are applied in the social sciences.

In grades 3–5, students will be building on the foundation laid in the primary grades. They will be taking their knowledge of addition and subtraction and connecting it to the study of multiplication and division. They will connect

division to the study of fractions. They will take what they have learned about identifying, building, and extending patterns to making predictions about patterns. Measurement in primary grades focused on nonstandard measures. Students will transfer that knowledge to working with standard measures. They will increase the sophistication of the study of data, probability, and statistics. Many of the concrete representations used in the primary grades will evolve to symbolic forms.

There are countless ways to make connections with the mathematics studied in these grades. For example, students enjoy taking surveys of their peers' preferences in food, music, movies, and games. This can be connected to collecting, organizing, and displaying the data in a way that makes sense — important skills that help students to better understand and interpret information presented in the world around them. Analyzing the data gathered from these surveys can be connected to interesting statistical problems. The teacher might pose the questions or have students generate their own.

Calculating the cost of having a class party that includes refreshments, prizes for games, and paper products is a relevant problem for intermediate age students. An activity of this type makes connections to a real world problem. Working in teams, students can estimate how much to order as they generate a menu and supplies that will be needed, and they can calculate costs to work within a given budget. This kind of problem also encourages them to do cost comparisons among various brands.

It is important for teachers to be conscious of connections that can be made in mathematics and to weave those connections into daily practice. When students are able to connect mathematical ideas both inside and outside of the classroom, they begin to see mathematics as a cohesive body of knowledge.

Intermediate Representation

REPRESENTATIONS PROVIDE VEHICLES for expressing and internalizing mathematical thought. They are a critical component in shaping the way students access, understand, express, and utilize mathematical ideas. Representations include physical objects, pictures, and symbols. They also include mental images, words, and ideas.

Representations can be formal or informal. Examples of formal representations are the conventional symbols, graphs, and diagrams traditionally introduced in school mathematics. Informal representations are often invented by students as a way of making sense of mathematical ideas and communicating those ideas to classmates or the teacher. Students should be allowed to create their own understanding and explanations to express relationships before more conventional representations are introduced. Connecting to their invented forms will facilitate a meaningful transition to thinking and communicating in the language of mathematics.

As teachers design lessons, choosing the representations they feel will best help students understand a concept becomes an important consideration. What shared mathematical language is needed to effectively communicate ideas? What manipulatives or models will be appropriate? How will students record their understanding of the concept? When is it appropriate to move from physical to symbolic representations?

In the intermediate grades students begin learning about multiplication conceptually, with concrete objects, often in groups or sets.

If there are 3 sets of marbles and there are 3 marbles in each set, how many marbles are there all together?

Students will use the marbles from the marble jar to make three groups and count the groups to discover there are 9. Students also learn they can represent that concept by drawing pictures of 3 marbles in three different groups. They extend that knowledge to represent the concept as repeated addition, writing $3 + 3 + 3 = 9$. In grades 3–5 students learn to represent the same situation as multiplication and write $3 \times 3 = 9$. This abstract equation makes sense to them because they have seen the connections through various representative models.

Intermediate grade students still continue to use non-conventional methods to help them interpret new concepts. For example, the teacher may pose the following problem.

Which is more, $\frac{1}{4}$ of a set of 16 items or $\frac{1}{3}$ of a set of 15 items?

Most students at this level do not yet have the means to approach this problem symbolically. Some students will use physical models, such as centimeter cubes to help them determine the answer. Many will make a drawing and will use various representations.

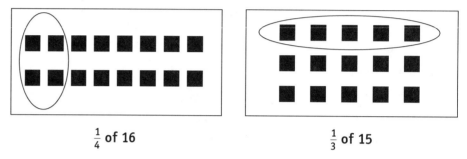

$\frac{1}{4}$ of 16 $\frac{1}{3}$ of 15

Students will be able to conclude that $\frac{1}{3}$ of 15 is a greater amount than $\frac{1}{4}$ of 16. This form of representation allows students to understand a process. It also provides an opportunity for the teacher to connect the visual representation with the equations $\frac{1}{3} \times 15 = 5$ and $\frac{1}{4} \times 16 = 4$ as another way of describing the results.

There are multiple representations for any mathematics concept. The greater the number of ways to represent the same idea, the greater the flexibility available in solving problems. For example, the number 25 can be thought of as 2 tens and 5 ones; as a quarter; as halfway between 1 and 50; as the square of 5; as an odd number; as one more than 24; as five less than 30; as 12 + 13; and so on. A student with access to this variety of representations of 25 is able to choose which version is useful for a particular situation.

One successful way to build multiple representations is to designate a number of the week and encourage students to build a repertoire of ways to represent that number. You might begin with a number such as 27, and ask students to find as many ways as they can to represent that number in 3 minutes. Record their findings on chart paper and post them for students to reflect upon. Revisit the problem for approximately 3 minutes each day. Encourage creative thinking by asking probing questions. *Is there a way to make 27 using multiplication AND division? Can 27 be made using three operations?* By the end of the week, you will have a chart full of interesting representations. If students engage in this type of activity on a regular basis, they will become fluid in their thinking about numbers.

20 + 7 = 27   9 + 18 = 27   (4 x 6) + 3 = 27
12 + 15 = 27   3 x 9 = 27   30 − 3 = 27
(5 x 5) + 2 = 27   (28 ÷ 4) + (2 x 10) = 27

Conclusion

The process standards are not an end, in and of themselves. Rather, they provide the advanced organizers or plan for lessons that present important mathematics content. Seeing connections among mathematical topics enables students to reason and make sense of new ideas and problem-solving situations they encounter. Through the process of communication, students are able to represent these new ideas either formally or informally.

Just as the process standards are interrelated, so are the process and content standards. For true mathematical thinking and learning to occur, both process and content need to be skillfully woven into and through each lesson. That is the goal to work toward.

Standard 1 **Number and Operation**

AT THE FIFTH GRADE LEVEL, number and operation include a lot of work with multiplication and division, and operations with fractions and decimals. Our lessons are derived from these important topics. They include a lesson that approaches the division algorithm informally, a lesson on subtracting mixed numbers, a lesson that uses 0, $\frac{1}{2}$, and 1 as benchmarks for estimating the fractional part of mixed numbers for estimation of sums and differences, and a lesson on subtracting decimals.

Three lessons model how the process standards can be used to teach content. A fourth lesson is a hypothetical textbook lesson that we have revised to be more standards based. These four lessons do not represent the entire curriculum, but rather provide glimpses of how, with a more concentrated effort to incorporate the process standards, better mathematics teaching and learning can be achieved.

One lesson we have chosen has as its ultimate purpose the teaching of the division algorithm for dividing a three-digit number by a one-digit number. By focusing on the process standard of problem solving, the typical approach of teaching the algorithm by rote is changed. Students are to develop informally their own understandings of the division process and apply these to the more formal learning of the algorithm that would follow this lesson. By making more connections to multiplication and through communication with class-mates, students can develop greater understanding of what division is and why the algorithm makes sense.

Another lesson we have chosen is on subtracting mixed numbers. Students are often taught this using mechanical methods. This lesson approaches the topic from a problem-solving angle. Through representations and communication, students create their own understanding of how mixed numbers are subtracted.

A third lesson we have chosen is on fractions. Students focus on the benchmarks 0, $\frac{1}{2}$, and 1 for common and uncommon fractions, within the context of estimating sums and differences of mixed numbers. By focusing on reasoning and proof, students develop strategies for determining which benchmark is appropriate for any given fraction.

The hypothetical textbook lesson we have chosen to revise is one that focuses on the subtraction of decimals to the thousandths place. This is a common lesson for this grade level, and one which is rarely presented beyond rote learning of the algorithm. In this revised lesson, students will use physical representations to model the subtraction, and be encouraged to communicate their perceived understandings of the subtraction and any connections that can be made to other subtraction situations.

Standard 1 Lessons

Using Multiplication
to Divide

Subtracting Mixed Numbers

Estimating Sums and
Differences Using Benchmarks

Subtracting Decimals

Using Multiplication to Divide

Introduction

Objective → Students will use their knowledge of how multiplication and division are related to solve division problems.

Context → Students have multiplied one-digit numbers by multiples of ten. They know multiplication and division facts. They are also familiar with remainders in division problems, using math facts. Students will go on to learn the long division algorithm for dividing three-digit numbers by one-digit and two-digit numbers.

NCTM Standards Focus

This lesson is one that is not typically presented in many programs. Instead, the division algorithm is usually presented as a rote process. The development of the algorithm is not addressed. By focusing on the following three process standards, a thoughtful and very useful lesson can be created to help students understand the division process.

Connections Students use their prior knowledge of multiplication facts and multiplying by multiples of ten to learn how to divide multi-digit dividends by one-digit divisors.

Problem Solving Students work out different methods for solving multi-digit division problems. Students apply problem-solving strategies they have learned for multiplication to the operation of division.

Communication Students make notes about the methods they used to solve problems and share their methods with the class during whole group discussion. They discuss and question the solution methods of their classmates and use what they learn to evaluate or adapt their own methods.

Teaching Plan

Materials → Student pages 22–23

WRITE THE NUMBERS 4, 28, and 7 on the overhead or the board. *How are these numbers related?* or *What four facts can be written using these numbers?* ($4 \times 7 = 28$, $7 \times 4 = 28$, $28 \div 4 = 7$, $28 \div 7 = 4$)

Next, write these numbers: 4, 280, 70. Have students describe how these numbers are related. Have them list the four facts. ($4 \times 70 = 280$, $70 \times 4 = 280$, $280 \div 4 = 70$, $280 \div 70 = 4$)

Ask students to tell how the two examples are related. Students should notice that the underlying facts are the same, but one factor and the product are different by a factor of 10.

CONTINUE THE LESSON BY PRESENTING the division problem $360 \div 9$. *How could you use multiplication to solve the problem?* Have students work in pairs to come up with ways in which multiplication can be used to solve the problem.

Methods Students Might Use

- Rearrange the problem. *What times 9 would equal 360?*
- Use the multiplication fact $4 \times 9 = 36$. Then use multiples of 10 to get $40 \times 9 = 360$.

What Might Happen . . . What to Do

Some students might have difficulty with the mental math component of this lesson. You might suggest that they use base ten | blocks. By making 9 equal-length rows so that the total number of blocks is 360, students can obtain the solution.

Have a brief class discussion in which students share their methods. Be sure that both methods listed are mentioned. You can relate the second method to the warm-up problems done at the beginning of the class.

Continue the lesson by having students work in pairs to solve these problems.

$$362 \div 9 \qquad 369 \div 9 \qquad 372 \div 9$$

INSTRUCT STUDENTS TO RECORD their methods, paying particular attention to how they used multiplication to obtain their solutions. Point out that remainders may be a part of the answer. Make sure that each of the following methods is introduced into the discussion.

362 ÷ 9

Possible Method Use multiplication facts and mental math to solve $360 \div 9$. The answer is 40. Using subtraction, $362 - 360 = 2$. Since 2 cannot be further divided by 9, the answer is 40 remainder 2.

369 ÷ 9

Possible Method We already know that $9 \times 40 = 360$. Using subtraction, $369 - 360 = 9$. Since 9 can be further divided by 9, and $9 \div 9 = 1$, then $369 \div 9 = 41$.

372 ÷ 9

Possible Method 1 Knowing that $9 \times 40 = 360$, subtraction yields $372 - 360 = 12$. Since 12 can be further divided by 9, and $12 \div 9 = 1$ remainder 3, the answer is 41 remainder 3.

Possible Method 2 From the prior problem, $369 \div 9 = 41$. Since 372 is greater than 369, the answer is at least 41. Subtracting gives $372 - 369 = 3$. Since 3 is less than 9, 3 is the remainder. The answer is 41 remainder 3.

It is important for students to recognize they used mental math as well as multiplication and division facts.

IN THEIR COMMUNICATIONS, students made connections to prior knowledge about math facts, as well as to informal rules in division. They also applied knowledge they gained from previous problems to later problems. Be sure to discuss how the problems build students' thinking one step at a time, from an answer that is a multiple of 10, to one that has a remainder, to one that has an answer that is not a multiple of 10, and finally to one that has an answer that is not a multiple of 10 and has a remainder.

Distribute page 22. Working individually or in pairs, instruct students to solve the problems using multiplication. Have them record their methods. Notice whether students are connecting the methods used to solve the earlier problems to solving these problems.

When students are finished, have them share their results and methods. Encourage them to question other students' thinking and methods when they do not agree with them. In all cases, the students' solution methods should show either a mental math or a partially mental math and paper/pencil activity.

Methods Students Might Use

- Rewrite the problem as $5 \times \square = 477$. Since $5 \times 90 = 450$, the answer is greater than 90. Subtracting from 477, $477 - 450 = 27$. Since 27 is greater than 5, the greatest multiple of 5 that is less than 27 is 25. So the answer is 95 remainder 2. That means that Brianna shelved 95 books each hour, plus 2 extra ones.

- Since $90 \times 5 = 450$ and $100 \times 5 = 500$, the answer must be between 90 and 100. We tried 95×5, which is 475. Subtracting that from 477 leaves 2. Since 2 is less than 5, it cannot be further divided by 5. So Brianna must have shelved 95 books each hour, plus an extra two books at some point.

The second problem can be solved using the same methods.

THE IMPORTANT PART OF THIS LESSON is that students attempt to solve the problems using multiplication as it relates to division. Students are not to develop their own process for solving division problems here, but to understand the connections between multiplication and division that were exemplified in the warm-up problems of this lesson. This knowledge will help students conceptually understand division and the process for solving it better. It will also help students understand the algorithm.

Extension

This lesson could also serve as a basis for dividing by a two-digit number. A problem such as $372 \div 40$ could be thought of as $40 \times$ what $= 372$. Similar reasoning to that used in this lesson could be applied to these problems.

Student Pages

Student page 22 contains two problems that can be used for the in-class activity. Students are to show how they solved the problems and write about their solution methods. Student page 23 contains practice problems that may be assigned for homework/individual practice.

Assessment

Your observations of the methods students used to explore multi-digit division and their explanations of those methods gave you the opportunity to assess whether they understood how to use multiplication facts, multiples of ten, and subtraction to solve division problems. Class discussion of methods and solutions also provided insights into students' progress. You can use the exercises on the student pages for additional assessment.

NCTM Standards Summary

By focusing on problem solving, students were able to develop their thinking about how multiplication can be used to help solve division problems. Students made connections between multiplication and division, how to think of division in terms of multiplication and how to use mental math and multiplication facts to solve division problems. As students developed their methods, they communicated these thoughts orally and through their writing.

Answers

Page 22
1. 95 books per hour, plus 2 more
2. 28 cups; 1 ounce left over

Page 23
1. 48; methods will vary
2. 95 marbles in each jar
3. 43 boxes
4. $96 for each class
5. 93 planters (6 seeds left)
6. 42 full tables

Using Multiplication to Divide

Solve each problem. Show the method or methods you used to solve it.

❶ Brianna spent 5 hours last week helping shelve books in the school library. She shelved a total of 477 books. She shelved the same number of books each hour. About how many books did she shelve per hour?

❷ Danny sold apple cider at the school's Fall Festival. The apple cider jug held 225 ounces. Danny sold the cider in 8 ounce cups. How many cups could he get from 1 jug, and how much cider was left?

Standard 1 Number and Operation

Using Multiplication to Divide

Solve each problem. Show your work.

❶ Use two different methods to solve 336 ÷ 7.

❷ Sarah and Kyle have collected 855 marbles. They stored them in 9 jars, with the same number of marbles in each jar. How many marbles are in each jar?

❸ In a grocery store, the stock people displayed the boxes of cereal on 5 shelves. There are 215 boxes all together. Each shelf has the same number of boxes. How many boxes of cereal are on each shelf?

❹ Six classes raised money for a field trip. They raised $576 in all. How much will each class get if they share the money equally?

❺ Frank and Shawna help out at a local nursery during spring vacation. They have a box with 750 tomato seeds. They plant 8 tomato seeds in each planter. How many planters can they fill?

❻ The cafeteria can hold 252 people seated at tables. Each table can seat 6 people. How many full tables can the cafeteria hold?

Subtracting Mixed Numbers

Introduction

Objective → Students will subtract mixed numbers having like denominators, regrouping when necessary.

Context → Students have had experience computing with proper fractions that have like denominators. They will go on to adding and subtracting mixed numbers with unlike denominators.

NCTM Standards Focus

Most of the time, students focus on the rules for computing with fractions, which they memorize. What happens, though, is that students are not given the opportunity to think about why the rules make sense. Presenting a more standards-based lesson, students will devise their own methods for subtracting mixed numbers with regrouping. Since they generate the methods, they will remember the processes and be able to recall and use them when needed.

Problem Solving Students apply their previous mathematical knowledge of computing with fractions to solve problems with mixed numbers. They reflect on the different ways to approach the problems and generalize from subtracting whole numbers and subtracting fractions to subtracting mixed numbers.

Representation Students represent the rational numbers either pictorially or symbolically. They find efficient ways to represent regrouping that make sense to them and that allow them to demonstrate their methods to the class.

Communication Students discuss the subtraction problems with their group members and write about solution methods they agree on. They share their strategies with their classmates as well as listen to and question the strategies of others. They assess the methods they see demonstrated and implement the ones that make sense to them.

Teaching Plan

Materials → Student pages 28–29

ARRANGE STUDENTS IN GROUPS of two to four. Quickly review subtracting proper fractions. Then talk with students about what happens when you subtract mixed numbers. Write these problems on the board.

$$4\frac{4}{5} - 2\frac{3}{5} = \qquad 8\frac{1}{3} - 3\frac{2}{3} =$$

$$6\frac{3}{8} - 4\frac{7}{8} = \qquad 7\frac{7}{10} - 6\frac{3}{10} =$$

Have students discuss how they would solve the first problem, $4\frac{4}{5} - 2\frac{3}{5}$. Some students might first subtract the whole numbers and then the fractions, while others might subtract the fractions first. Ask them to review how they subtract whole numbers. Have students volunteer that since no regrouping is necessary and the numbers are small, this problem can be done mentally.

Have students look at the second problem, $6\frac{3}{8} - 4\frac{7}{8}$, tell what they notice, and suggest approaches they might take. *Can this problem be solved by subtracting the whole numbers first? Why or why not?* After a short discussion, have students return to their groups and solve the remaining three problems. Encourage them to record their solution processes and show how they represented the mixed numbers.

OBSERVE STUDENTS AS THEY SOLVE the subtraction problems. If some students have difficulties getting started, discuss with them how they can write a whole as a fraction. Ask them what denominator they would use for a problem that deals with eighths. Keep encouraging the students with questions, but do not tell them what to do.

After students have solved the subtraction problems, bring the class together. Have them communicate their solution processes. All students are involved in the communication process as they listen to others' ideas and integrate these ideas into their own thinking.

Methods Students Might Use

- To do the problem $6\frac{3}{8} - 4\frac{7}{8}$, students might represent the fractions pictorially.

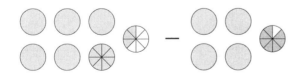

- Using the subtraction algorithm for whole numbers, moving right to left, students represented $6\frac{3}{8}$ by regrouping the whole number, adding the regrouped 1 ($\frac{8}{8}$) to the existing $\frac{3}{8}$, and getting a new minuend of $5\frac{11}{8}$.

$$5\frac{11}{8}$$
$$6\frac{\cancel{3}}{8}$$
$$-\ 4\frac{7}{8}$$
$$\overline{1\frac{4}{8} = 1\frac{1}{2}}$$

What Might Happen . . . What to Do

- -

Some students might regroup the mixed number, but use a base-ten place-value concept and show the subtraction sentence as $6\frac{3}{8} - 2\frac{7}{8} = 5\frac{13}{8} - 2\frac{7}{8} = 3\frac{6}{8} = 3\frac{3}{4}$.

Have students use models to show the regrouped ones as equivalent fractions in the different subtraction problems.

HAVE STUDENTS WHO REPRESENTED the fractions with pictures and pictorially solved the subtraction problems introduce their methods to the class. Then ask students who did not solve the problems pictorially to do at least one problem using this method. Encourage students who used symbolic expressions to solve the problems to tell the class what they did and why. Remind students that it is important to reduce answers to lowest terms.

After different symbolic representations have been introduced to the class, you might want to encourage students who used pictorial methods to invent their own algorithms or use the ones their classmates shared with them. Finally, have students compare their original methods with the new methods they tried. Ask them to tell which ones they preferred and why.

Have students then solve $9 - 2\frac{5}{6} = \underline{\quad}$ individually. Encourage them to use the methods they developed in their groups or saw during class discussion. Remind them to show the steps they go through when solving the problem.

What Might Happen . . . What to Do

- -

Some students might perceive this problem as being very different from the mixed number problems. Suggest that students write a fraction after 9. *For this problem,*

what would the denominator be? (6) *How many sixths are there in addition to the 9?* (0) Write $9\frac{0}{6}$, and ask students how they can proceed.

When students have solved the problem, ask what methods they used and why they decided on that particular approach. *How was this problem the same as the previous ones? How was it different?* Give as many students as possible an opportunity to defend their representations and solution processes with the class.

Student Pages

The problems on student page 28 involve subtraction with mixed numbers. Encourage students to show their work with drawings and written commentary. Student page 29 has practice and application problems that students can solve pictorially or symbolically.

Assessment

You have observed students as they developed different methods to solve subtraction problems with like denominators. Some of the subtraction problems required regrouping before solving. The students' responses showed how well they understood whole-to-part relationships that exist in regrouping problems.

NCTM Standards Summary

Students used problem solving and prior knowledge of proper fractions and subtracting whole numbers. They used representation to show mixed numbers pictorially or symbolically in order to carry out the subtraction of rational numbers with regrouping. They shared their methods and strategies with the class using communication. After listening to each other's methods, they tried one another's representations to evaluate the reliability and efficiency of the different approaches.

Answers

Page 28

1. $\frac{1}{2}$
2. $1\frac{4}{5}$
3. $\frac{1}{4}$
4. $2\frac{1}{3}$

Page 29

1. $3\frac{2}{7}$
2. 1
3. $1\frac{4}{5}$
4. $3\frac{1}{3}$
5. $2\frac{2}{11}$
6. $3\frac{7}{8}$
7. $3\frac{2}{3}$
8. $6\frac{2}{3}$
9. $3\frac{1}{2}$ inches
10. $3\frac{7}{12}$ feet
11. $1\frac{3}{8}$ cups
12. $21\frac{1}{5}$ miles

Subtracting Mixed Numbers

Solve the problems. Show how you represented the mixed numbers and how you subtracted.

❶ $2\frac{1}{4} - 1\frac{3}{4}$

❷ $3\frac{2}{5} - 1\frac{3}{5}$

❸ $1\frac{7}{8} - 1\frac{5}{8}$

❹ $5\frac{1}{6} - 2\frac{5}{6}$

Standard 1 Number and Operation

Subtracting Mixed Numbers

Solve the problems. Show your work.

❶ $6\frac{4}{7} - 3\frac{2}{7}$

❷ $3\frac{1}{2} - 2\frac{1}{2}$

❸ $7\frac{3}{5} - 5\frac{4}{5}$

❹ $4\frac{5}{9} - 1\frac{2}{9}$

❺ $5\frac{9}{11} - 3\frac{7}{11}$

❻ $7\frac{1}{8} - 3\frac{2}{8}$

❼ $8\frac{1}{3} - 4\frac{2}{3}$

❽ $6\frac{5}{6} - \frac{1}{6}$

Solve each problem. Write the number sentence. Tell how you solved the problem.

❾ Terry bought a bookmark that is $5\frac{1}{4}$ inches long. The tassel is $1\frac{3}{4}$ inches long. How long is the marker itself?

❿ Jamahl is $6\frac{5}{12}$ feet tall. He uses a measuring tape that is 10 feet long. How much longer is the measuring tape than Jamahl?

⓫ Erin is making cornbread. She uses $2\frac{5}{8}$ cups of milk in the recipe. She pours the milk from a full quart (4 cups). How much milk does she have left?

⓬ Maria lives 30 miles from her cousin Juan. Their grandmother lives between them, $8\frac{4}{5}$ miles from Maria. How far is it from Juan's house to their grandmother's house?

Standard 1 Number and Operation

Estimating Sums and Differences Using Benchmarks

Introduction

Objective → Students will learn to estimate fractions to either 0, $\frac{1}{2}$, or 1. They will use this knowledge to estimate sums and differences of mixed numbers.

Context → Students understand the concept of fractions and know how to add and subtract fractions with like denominators. Students will continue to learn about finding exact sums and differences of mixed numbers with unlike denominators.

NCTM Standards Focus

Some lessons have students estimate sums or differences of mixed numbers using whole numbers only. By doing so, the fractional concepts are trivialized. This lesson includes $\frac{1}{2}$ as a third benchmark. This requires much more thought about number sense concepts related to fractions, which should be the goal when working in a unit devoted to fractions. Instead of simply directing students to round to 0, $\frac{1}{2}$, or 1, a more standards-based lesson has students develop their own methods for determining the closest benchmark. By focusing on the following three process standards, a more thoughtful fraction-estimation lesson can be presented.

Reasoning and Proof Students develop methods that they can use to determine if a fraction is closer to 0, $\frac{1}{2}$, or 1. They examine and discuss their own ideas and those of their classmates, evaluate these ideas, and determine whether suggested methods work.

Connections Students use and build on their prior knowledge of fractions and rounding whole numbers to help them decide the appropriate benchmark for each fraction.

Communication Students communicate their ideas about fractions and corresponding benchmarks and serve as the audience for each other's comments. They discuss and question their classmates on the strategies they used to determine benchmarks and then use this information to evaluate their own methods.

Teaching Plan

Materials → Student pages 34–35

PEOPLE OFTEN MUST WORK with uncommon fractions, for example in the stock market or when measuring something. Explain to the class that sometimes they will have to add or subtract uncommon fractions and mixed numbers such as $4\frac{15}{16} + 2\frac{1}{7}$. Point out that as with whole numbers, they don't always need to find an exact answer to each problem; often an estimate is enough. One way to estimate with uncommon fractions is to find benchmarks for these fractions. The benchmarks they will be using in this lesson are 0, $\frac{1}{2}$, and 1.

Write the following fractions on the board.

$$\frac{1}{8} \qquad \frac{5}{6} \qquad \frac{3}{5} \qquad \frac{2}{5} \qquad \frac{9}{10}$$

(Answers: 0, 1, $\frac{1}{2}$, $\frac{1}{2}$, 1)

Have students work in groups to decide which benchmark (0, $\frac{1}{2}$, or 1)
each fraction is closest to. Encourage students to look for methods they can
use to solve the problem. Tell students to record their representations,
reasoning, and proof, because they will need to convince the class that their
answers are correct and that their methods make sense. While students work
together, visit each group. If some students get stuck, suggest one or more
of the following methods. In the end, make sure that all five methods have
been pointed out to the students.

Methods Students Might Use

- Drawing a circle or rectangle and shading the part the fraction represents.
- Using the denominator of the fraction to find the halfway point (and
  maybe the $\frac{1}{4}$ or $\frac{3}{4}$ point). For example, in evaluating $\frac{1}{8}$, students can set
  the halfway point at $\frac{4}{8}$ and see that $\frac{1}{8}$ is closer to $\frac{0}{8}$ than to $\frac{4}{8}$.
- Using equivalent fractions. For example, by changing $\frac{3}{5}$ to $\frac{6}{10}$, they can
  find the halfway point more easily.
- Using a number line and placing the fractions on it.
- Changing the fractions into decimals, especially when the fractions
  can easily be converted to dollars and cents. For example, students might
  convert $\frac{9}{10}$ to 9 dimes or $0.90 to show that the benchmark for $\frac{9}{10}$ is 1.

When students come back, have them share their results. Here are some
things students should have noticed.

- Some of the fractions, such as $\frac{1}{8}$ and $\frac{9}{10}$, were simple to benchmark.
- With other fractions, students had to set a cut-off point to decide which
  benchmark to use. For example, is $\frac{1}{4}$ closer to 0 or $\frac{1}{2}$? Is $\frac{3}{4}$ closer to
  $\frac{1}{2}$ or 1?

IT IS IMPORTANT TO MAKE SURE that this discussion introduces
different techniques and representations to the class. As they are sharing
their methods and representations, encourage students to prove to the class
that their methods work. During the discussion, ask students why they prefer
certain methods and why some methods work better than others in certain
situations.

f.y.i.

Review rounding whole numbers
to help your class connect fraction benchmarks to their prior
knowledge of rounding whole
numbers. Focus specifically on
relating the benchmarks for
fractions to students' prior
knowledge of rounding to 0, 50,
or 100. Give students several
whole numbers (15, 63, 87,
for example) and have them
describe how they would round
these numbers to 0, 50, or 100.
Discuss with the class how 0
relates to the 0 benchmark for
fractions, 50 to the $\frac{1}{2}$, and
100 to the 1.

Now that students have some methods they can use, give them the following fractions to estimate.

$$\frac{1}{4} \qquad \frac{7}{9} \qquad \frac{8}{13} \qquad \frac{17}{55}$$

(Answers: $\frac{1}{2}$, 1, $\frac{1}{2}$, $\frac{1}{2}$)

THIS GROUP OF FRACTIONS will challenge your students in at least two ways. Some of the fractions are close to or at the $\frac{1}{4}$ or $\frac{3}{4}$ point, and some of them are uncommon. Encourage students to try several of the methods they learned during the class discussion or to develop new ones. Remind them to record what they do.

What Might Happen . . . What to Do

Students might disagree about what benchmark to use for $\frac{1}{4}$ or $\frac{3}{4}$. You might suggest to them that this is similar to rounding numbers like 25 and 75 to 0, 50, or 100. Have students decide how they would round the whole numbers and then discuss how the decision can be transferred to fractions. Point out that sometimes it is important when estimating to decide first whether the situation calls for estimating on the low side (rounding down) or on the high side (rounding up).

After students have decided on benchmarks for each fraction, bring them back together to discuss their results. For fractions such as the last two, the students may have used a method of adjusting the fractions to make them easier to work with. For example, $\frac{8}{13}$ is about $\frac{8}{12}$, which is equivalent to $\frac{2}{3}$. Also, $\frac{17}{55}$ is about $\frac{17}{51}$, which is equivalent to $\frac{1}{3}$. In both cases, the adjusted fractions are somewhat greater than the original fractions, but neither of the original fractions will fall outside the $\frac{1}{4}$ to $\frac{3}{4}$ range.

To conclude the lesson, tell students that they will use their benchmarking skills to estimate sums and differences. Give them the following addition and subtraction problems and have students estimate the answers.

$$5\frac{1}{2} + 4\frac{1}{7} \qquad\qquad 1\frac{18}{19} - \frac{3}{4}$$

$$8\frac{3}{19} + 2\frac{14}{27} \qquad\qquad 6\frac{5}{21} - 4\frac{10}{11}$$

(Answers: $5\frac{1}{2} + 4 = 9\frac{1}{2}$, $2 - 1 = 1$, $8 + 2\frac{1}{2} = 10\frac{1}{2}$, $6 - 5 = 1$)

Student Pages

The exercises on student page 34 offer students practice in determining whether fractions that are close to $\frac{1}{2}$ in value are greater or less than $\frac{1}{2}$ and in deciding whether some common and uncommon fractions are closer to 0, $\frac{1}{2}$, or 1.

Student page 35 provides practice in estimating sums and differences using benchmarks and problems where they apply their estimation skills.

Assessment

Your observations of the group and the whole-class discussions gave you many opportunities to assess students' understanding. You observed how students connected fraction benchmarks to their prior knowledge of rounding whole numbers. By challenging your students to justify their methods and techniques for determining benchmarks, you evaluated their reasoning and how they proved which benchmark (0, $\frac{1}{2}$, or 1) each fraction was closest to. During their sharing, particular attention was given to how students convinced other students that their methods worked, whether they questioned methods and techniques that did not make sense, and why some methods worked better than others in certain situations. The exercises on the student pages also provide opportunities with which to assess students individually.

NCTM Standards Summary

In this lesson, students focused on the NCTM process standards of reasoning and proof, connections, and communication. By reasoning and proving their answers and methods, students focused on number sense concepts by developing their own strategies to determine if a fraction is closer to 0, $\frac{1}{2}$, or 1. They connected their prior knowledge of fractions, whole numbers, and the process of rounding to the concept of benchmarking common and uncommon fractions.

In addition to developing their own methods and strategies for determining benchmarks for fractions, students explained and defended their methods and strategies to their classmates. By convincing their classmates of their methods, by questioning the strategies used by other students, and then by evaluating their own methods, students experienced the value and importance of communicating their reasoning.

Answers

Page 34

1. Greater than $\frac{1}{2}$ or $> \frac{1}{2}$
2. Less than $\frac{1}{2}$ or $< \frac{1}{2}$
3. $> \frac{1}{2}$
4. $> \frac{1}{2}$
5. $> \frac{1}{2}$
6. $\frac{5}{12}$; Explanations will vary.
7. $\frac{16}{17}$; Explanations will vary.

Page 35

1. $5 + 7\frac{1}{2} = 12\frac{1}{2}$
2. $2 - 1 = 1$
3. $4\frac{1}{2} - 4 = \frac{1}{2}$
4. $4 + 4\frac{1}{2} = 8\frac{1}{2}$
5. $2\frac{1}{2} - 2\frac{1}{2} = 0$
6. $4\frac{1}{2} + 4\frac{1}{2} = 9$
7. There are less students with 3 or more vowels. Since there are about $\frac{1}{2}$ with 3 or more vowels and about $\frac{1}{2}$ with 2 vowels in their first names, there are few students with one vowel.
8. $0 + 0 + 1\frac{1}{2} + 2 + 1\frac{1}{2} = 5$
9. Tuesday; $\frac{1}{2}$ mark more
10. Explanations will vary.

Estimating Sums and Differences Using Benchmarks

Show each fraction on the number line. Then tell whether each fraction is greater than or less than $\frac{1}{2}$.

❶ $\frac{2}{3}$

0                  $\frac{1}{2}$ 1

❷ $\frac{5}{11}$

0                  $\frac{1}{2}$ 1

❸ $\frac{6}{10}$

0                  $\frac{1}{2}$ 1

❹ $\frac{13}{25}$

0                  $\frac{1}{2}$ 1

❺ $\frac{48}{92}$

0                  $\frac{1}{2}$ 1

Read the problem and circle the answer.

❻ Almost one half of the class is going to art. Circle the fraction that shows the fraction of students going to art. Explain your answer.

$\frac{4}{5}$ $\frac{1}{6}$ $\frac{5}{12}$ $\frac{4}{7}$

❼ Bryan used almost a whole pound of cheese to make cheese sandwiches. Which fraction tells how much cheese he used? Tell why.

$\frac{16}{17}$ $\frac{1}{11}$ $\frac{4}{13}$ $\frac{13}{42}$

Standard 1 Number and Operation

Estimating Sums and Differences Using Benchmarks

Estimate the sum or difference. Show how you thought about each number.

1 $4\frac{3}{4} + 7\frac{3}{5} =$

2 $1\frac{16}{17} - \frac{35}{36} =$

3 $4\frac{13}{23} - 4\frac{5}{36} =$

4 $3\frac{12}{13} + 4\frac{11}{26} =$

5 $2\frac{1}{3} - 2\frac{1}{4} =$

6 $4\frac{7}{16} + 4\frac{7}{27} =$

Solve. Use what you know about benchmarks.

7 In Cecilia's class, $\frac{7}{26}$ of the students have three or more vowels in their first names, $\frac{3}{5}$ have two vowels, and the rest have one vowel.

- Compare the fractions. Are there more or less students with three or more vowels in their first names than students with two vowels in their first names?

- How do you know if there are many or few students with one vowel in their first names?

8 The price of a stock listed on the stock market rose $\frac{5}{128}$ points on Monday, $\frac{7}{32}$ on Tuesday, $1\frac{9}{16}$ on Wednesday, $1\frac{7}{8}$ on Thursday, and $1\frac{37}{128}$ points on Friday. About how many points did the price of this stock increase during the week?

9 While travelling, Leila exchanges U.S. dollars for the local currency. On Monday, she got $5\frac{11}{18}$ marks for each dollar. On Tuesday, she got $5\frac{23}{24}$ marks for each dollar. Which day did she get more marks for a dollar? Tell how much more.

10 What is the benchmark for $\frac{3}{12}$? Explain your reasoning.

Subtracting Decimals

Introduction

Objective → Students will subtract decimals through the thousandths place.

Context → Students have previously added and subtracted decimals to the hundredths place. This lesson comes at the end of a unit on addition and subtraction of decimal numbers and is followed by lessons on the multiplication of decimals.

Subtracting Decimals

Learn

A scientist is conducting an experiment. She has a rock that has a mass of 1.363 kilograms. After she runs her experiment she measures the mass again. Now the mass is 1.225. How much mass did the rock lose during the experiment?

Find $1.363 - 1.225$.

Step 1

Record:

Line up the decimal points.

$$
\begin{array}{r}
1\,.\ 363 \\
-1\,.\ 225 \\
\hline
\end{array}
$$

Step 2

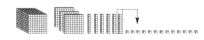

Record:

$$
\begin{array}{r}
{}^{5\ 13} \\
1.3\cancel{6}\cancel{3} \\
-1.225 \\
\hline
0.138
\end{array}
$$

Regroup 1 hundredth into thousandths.

Subtract.

Place a decimal point in the difference.

The rock lost 0.138 kilograms of mass.

Try

Examples

A.
$$
\begin{array}{r}
{}^{7\ 10} \\
3.\cancel{8}\cancel{0} \\
-0.53 \\
\hline
3.27
\end{array}
$$

B.
$$
\begin{array}{r}
{}^{4\ 10} \\
2.\cancel{5}\cancel{0}4 \\
-0.241 \\
\hline
2.263
\end{array}
$$

C.
$$
\begin{array}{r}
{}^{9\ 13} \\
\cancel{10}.\cancel{3}87 \\
-9.522 \\
\hline
0.865
\end{array}
$$

D.
$$
\begin{array}{r}
{}^{4\ 10} \\
0.1\cancel{5}\cancel{0} \\
-0.024 \\
\hline
0.126
\end{array}
$$

Explain what happened in example B.

NCTM Process Standards Analysis and Focus

The standards analysis examines how the process standards have been incorporated into the above lesson. By increasing the focus on three of the process standards, a more effective and meaningful lesson can be presented. The suggestions offered can help you to think about how this might be accomplished.

Connections The lesson asks students to connect to their knowledge of decimal place value to subtract decimals through thousandths.

Suggestion → Encourage students to make connections between the renaming process applied in subtracting whole numbers and subtracting with decimals. Reinforce the need to align decimal points by connecting the procedure to students' knowledge of place value.

Try

Find the difference.

1. $4.35 - 0.757$ **2.** $6.2 - 3.941$ **3.** $0.7 - 0.088$

4. 3.07 -0.68	**5.** 5.3 -3.157	**6.** 13.222 -8.737	**7.** 3.28 -0.566
8. 5.53 -3.11	**9.** 3.4 -1.754	**10.** 7.725 -4.97	**11.** 12.448 -8.123

12. $2.54 - 1.29$ **13.** $2.4 - 0.433$ **14.** $3.2 - 2.3$

15. $4.96 - 2.993$ **16.** $3.8 - 1.724$ **17.** $6.32 - 1.275$

Problem Solving

Use the table for problems 18–20.

18. How many more points would Gina need to tie Alexandra?

19. How many more points did Tina score that Sonja?

20. Last year the winner scored 9.902 points. How many more points was that than this year's winner?

Floor Exercise	
Contestant	Score
Sonja	9.813 seconds
Gina	8.524 seconds
Alexandra	9.176 seconds
Tina	8.942 seconds

Representation The lesson uses place-value blocks to represent the regrouping that occurs in subtracting decimals through thousandths.

Suggestion → Emphasize the role the decimal point plays in our place-value system. Compare the value represented by digits in a whole number and the value of the same digits after a decimal point is inserted into the number. Examine adding zeros to the right of the decimal point as well as to the right of digits after the decimal point.

Communication The lesson offers few opportunities for students to discuss the regrouping procedure or their understanding of the role place value plays in the exchange process.

Suggestion → Initiate discussions in which students communicate their understanding of subtraction and regrouping with both whole numbers and decimals using the exacting language of place value. Communicating their understanding will reinforce the connections made in the lesson and activate student reasoning.

Problem Solving The problem-solving section asks students to use information from a table to solve problems involving decimal computations.

Reasoning and Proof Students are asked to explain regrouping for a specific digit in a subtraction example.

The teaching plan that follows shows how the suggestions for increasing the focus on the process standards can be implemented.

Revised Teaching Plan

f.y.i.

Aligning the decimal points when writing decimal addition and subtraction vertically can be learned as a rote rule or learned with understanding. If you suspect students have just memorized a rule and bypassed real understanding of place value and decimal operations, try connecting this "rule" back to whole-number place value. *If we write the problem 43 − 2 vertically, why do we write the 2 directly under the 3? Why don't we put it under the 4?*

Encouraging and modeling place-value language has a large role to play here. It is important that students understand that the decimal point acts as a separator—it separates the ones place from the tenths place, the whole numbers from amounts less than one.

BEGIN THE LESSON BY WRITING the following two subtraction exercises side by side, horizontally, on the board: 6532 − 4578 and 6.532 − 4.578. Instruct students to read both problems aloud, making sure they say the decimal values for the decimals rather than reading the numbers as "six point five three two." Have students discuss the similarities and differences between the two problems. Draw attention to the fact that though the numerals that make up the numbers are the same, the insertion of the decimal point changes the values they represent.

$$6532 - 4578 \qquad 6.532 - 4.578$$

Tell students to copy the problems so they can solve them. *Did you write the problems on your paper the way I wrote them on the board? Why?* Students should relate that they placed 4578 below 6532 because they needed to line up the ones, tens, hundreds, and thousands. If students say they lined up the decimal points for 6.532 − 4.587, ask them why they did this. *What is the function or purpose of the decimal point?* (It separates the ones from the tenths, the whole number from amounts that are less than one.) These questions reinforce what students learned when they subtracted with tenths and with hundredths. They also focus students' thinking on what they are actually doing as they align the numbers.

DISCUSS SIMILARITIES AND DIFFERENCES between the two problems and their answers. Students should see the similarity in the mechanics of the algorithm. Make sure they realize that the thinking for regrouping across the decimal point and regrouping with decimal numbers is the same as with whole numbers: it is an exchange of one for ten. *Are the numbers in both answers are the same? What effect does the decimal point have on the answer?* (Placing the decimal point in the appropriate place in the answer changes the value of what each digit represents.)

Tell students they are going to look at some situations that may seem trickier, but if they remember the importance of lining up the digits in the appropriate places, they should be able to handle these problems.

START BY HAVING THE STUDENTS SUBTRACT two tenths from one (1.0 − 0.2). Either dictate the problem or write it horizontally on the board. Have students write the problem horizontally, and then have them write it vertically. *How did you line up the numbers? Why did you line them up that way?* Make sure students align the digits in the place-value columns that they represent. Reviewing this information with each problem reinforces the importance of this procedure in the subtraction process. Have the students work the problem and discuss their answers.

What Might Happen . . . What to Do

Students may be confused by the zeros in the ones place and tenths place. Make sure students understand that 1.0 is 1 and no tenths, which is still equal to 1. Discuss the fact that placing a decimal point to the right of the ones place of any whole number and adding zeros does not change the value of the number. The same is true of adding zeros to the right of digits on the right side of the decimal point. For example, 3.5 and 3.50 have the same value. You might compare 3 dollars and 5 dimes with 3 dollars and 50 pennies. Also point out that 0.2 is 0 and 2 tenths, which equals .2. In fact, the standard convention with decimals is to put a zero in the ones place if there is no digit in a place greater than the tenths place.

3.5   =   3.50

WRITE 537 − 12 AND 537 − 1.2 ON THE BOARD. Instruct students to copy the first problem but not to solve it. *How did you arrange the numbers when you wrote this problem?* Have them copy the second problem. *Where did you place decimal points when you wrote the second problem? Why?* Focusing on the placement of the decimal point here can help prevent the error of aligning both numbers at the right as is done when no decimal points are involved

Instruct students to work both problems and compare their answers as you discuss their results. This pair of problems focuses attention on the role of the decimal point and reinforces its effect on the place value of the digits. These problems also offer an opportunity to check that students understand that adding zeros to the right of the decimal point does not change the value of the numbers.

Present 6.5 − 2.37 and 65 − 2.37. Ask students to copy these problems and discuss how they arranged the numbers before having students complete the subtraction. Be sure to discuss the solutions. Extend to the thousandths place by presenting a problem such as 42 − 0.443.

Conclude the lesson by having students work a few more problems to assess readiness for the practice assignment.

Student Pages

Students are now ready to complete practice exercises similar to those shown on the reduced student pages.

Assessment

As students discussed how they set up the problems and described solutions, there were ample opportunities to determine whether they understood the importance of place value and lining up the digits to subtract with decimals.

NCTM Standards Summary

While having as many as four digits to the right of the decimal point may be unfamiliar, students in the fifth grade have extensive experience with the base-ten number system. Making strong connections to prior knowledge of place-value representation and familiar procedures used with subtracting whole numbers helped students understand that the same principles apply when subtraction involves decimals. Communication was important as students continually described how they used place value to line up numbers. Dialogue about the role of the decimal point gave students a clear understanding of the reason for lining up decimal points.

Standard 2 **Algebra**

AT THE FIFTH GRADE LEVEL, algebra includes a lot of work with the four basic operations as well as mental math, variables in expressions and equations, and the coordinate system. Our lessons are derived from these important topics. They include a lesson on using properties to facilitate mental math calculations, a lesson on evaluating variable expressions, a lesson on ordered pairs and finding the horizontal or vertical distance between two points, and a lesson on addition and subtraction as opposite operations to solve equations.

Three lessons model how the process standards can be used to teach content. A fourth lesson is a hypothetical textbook lesson that we have revised to be more standards based. These four lessons do not represent the entire curriculum, but rather provide glimpses of how, with a more concentrated effort to incorporate the process standards, better mathematics teaching and learning can be achieved.

One lesson we have chosen focuses on developing students' ability to do mental math calculations. Through the process standards of problem solving, communication, and connections, students discuss their strategies for performing calculations mentally. They realize how the commutative, associative, and distributive properties are useful in being able to make calculations without pencil and paper.

Another lesson we have chosen has students evaluate variable expressions and identify the value that makes a sentence true. Using the process standards of representation, reasoning and proof, and connections, students realize how efficient using a variable can be. They use tables to show values of an expression for different values of the variable, and use these tables to find solutions to number sentences.

A third lesson we have chosen has students find patterns in a set of ordered pairs and find horizontal and vertical distances. This lesson is driven by the process standards of representation and reasoning and proof, as students plot ordered pairs as points and write ordered pairs for given points. Students predict ordered pairs that extend a pattern, and determine how to find the distance between two points on a horizontal or vertical line.

The hypothetical textbook lesson we have chosen to revise is one that uses the opposite operations of addition and subtraction to solve equations. Through better incorporation of the process standards of reasoning and proof, connections, and representation, students use manipulatives to develop a deeper understanding of the inverse relationship between addition and subtraction.

Standard 2 Lessons

Using Algebraic Properties

Using Expressions

Exploring Ordered Pairs

Exploring Inverses: Addition and Subtraction

Using Algebraic Properties

Introduction

Objective → Students will apply the commutative, associative, and distributive properties to solve problems.

Context → Students know the basic algorithms for the four operations and have some experience with estimation and mental math. This lesson will enable them to do more complex mental math and will serve as preparation for simplifying algebraic expressions in equations.

NCTM Standards Focus

Understanding the properties of numbers leads to improved performance in mathematics in many ways. Students who understand how numbers behave are able to do calculations and use estimation strategies fluidly and effectively. They develop a sense of number understanding that there are many ways to think about computation. In this standards-based lesson, students are given opportunities to develop and apply mental math strategies using the commutative, associative, and distributive properties.

Problem Solving Students determine what strategies to use to solve different problems.

Reasoning and Proof Using their knowledge of different properties and their number sense, students devise strategies for using estimation and mental math to solve problems.

Communication Students discuss the best mental math strategies for specific situations. They explain their thinking to a larger group, and evaluate each other's strategies.

Teaching Plan

Materials → Student pages 48–49

PRESENT THE FOLLOWING PROBLEMS one at a time to the class as a whole. Discuss the mental math solution methods that students propose. It is important to remember that different students use different strategies and are more comfortable with some than others. However, hearing the strategies of others provides opportunities for students to learn new strategies or refine ones they already use. The strategies suggested here are only examples of ways to solve the problems.

Problem 1

A person wants to know the cost of 5 hot dogs at $1.97 each, plus 5 orders of fries at $0.53 cents each. *What mental math strategies could you use to solve this problem?*

Some students may quickly see that since there are the same number of hot dogs and fries, they can find the combined cost of a hot dog and an order of fries ($1.97 + $0.53 = $2.50) and then multiply by 5. In this case they would be using the distributive property which states that $a(b + c) = ab + ac$. Again using the distributive property, students might reason that $5 \times \$2.50 = 5 \times \$2.00 + 5 \times \$0.50 = \$10.00 + \$2.50 = \$12.50$.

Problem 2

A person has four items in his or her cart. The prices of the items are $0.74, $0.32, $0.26, and $0.28. *How much will they cost? How could you solve this problem using mental math?*

Students might use their knowledge of the commutative $(a + b = b + a)$ and associative $[a + (b + c) = (a + b) + c]$ properties for addition to rearrange and regroup the addends to make it easier to find the sum $0.74 + $0.32 + $0.26 + $0.28. For example, students could add $0.74 and $0.26 to get $1.00, add $0.32 and $0.28 to get $0.60, and add $1.00 and $0.60 to get $1.60. Encourage students to analyze problems to look for ways to make computation easier as they solve problems. This will not only save time, but decrease the chances for making errors.

Problem 3

A student wants to buy 3 drinks at $0.99 each and 4 bags of popcorn at $1.43 each. *Will $10.00 be enough?*

Before they begin solving the problem, ask students to look at it carefully. *What is the problem asking you to find out?* (Is $10.00 enough?) *Do you need to know exactly how much 3 drinks and 4 bags of popcorn cost?* (No. You need to know if the items cost more or less than $10.00.) Students should realize that it is not always necessary to calculate an exact answer. *About how much will the drinks cost?* (About $3.00, but not more than $3.00) *About how much will the popcorn cost?* (About $4 \times \$1.50$, but not more than $6.00). Students should realize that since they have rounded up they can be sure the actual amount is less. The items cannot cost more than $6.00 + $3.00, or $9.00. $10.00 is more than enough.

CONTINUE THE LESSON by reviewing some different methods for doing mental math. Distribute student page 48 and ask students to work in pairs or small groups. Instruct them to solve the problems using mental math or estimation. Tell them to make notes so they can explain their methods.

f.y.i.

You may wish to talk to the students about the difference between mental math and estimation. Estimation refers to finding an approximate answer. Mental math refers to finding an exact answer using only the mind. While it is not crucial that they memorize definitions for the terms, it is important that they have a conceptual understanding of both and know when to use them.

What Might Happen . . . What to Do

Students might have difficulty naming the property that they use. The most important point here is that they understand what the different properties allow them to do and not do. Use your judgment of the class's understanding of the properties and your own goals in determining how important it is to call out the names of the properties.

When the groups are finished, bring the class together and ask students to discuss their solutions and methods. Encourage students to question each other to be sure that they understand the method being presented. Some possible solutions and methods follow.

Methods Students Might Use

1. Charlene might first use the associative property to combine the small popcorn with the large cereal bar to get $2.00. Then she might add the two juices to get $1.80 and then add the two subtotals to get $3.80. The commutative property tells her she can add the items in any order.

2. Shamina could use a number of strategies. She might combine 1 large popcorn and 1 large cereal bar to get $3.00, multiply by 2 to get the cost of 2 popcorns and 2 cereal bars, and then add the third large popcorn to get the answer of $7.75.

3. Nick can add the price of 2 medium juices and 1 small cereal bar to get $2.75. He can continue adding another $2.75 until he gets close to $8.00. Since $2.75 + $2.75 = $5.50, he can see that 2 groups of 2 medium juices for each small cereal bar is the most he can buy.

4. Carlos can add the price of a small juice and a small popcorn and see that together they cost $1.35. He can then figure out that $1.35 multiplied by 6 is the same as $(6 \times \$1.00) + (6 \times \$0.35)$ or $6.00 + $2.10 or $8.10. He doesn't have enough to get each person his or her own juice and popcorn. However, he could buy everyone a small juice and have more than $4.00 left. If two people share a medium popcorn everyone can have juice and popcorn.

Conclude the lesson by assigning student page 49.

Student Pages

Student page 48 contains the problems to be used for the in-class activity. Student page 49 gives students additional problem-solving situations in which they can use mental math and estimation.

Assessment

Students demonstrated their estimation and mental math abilities as they discussed their solution methods for the problems in the lesson. You were able to assess students' ability to explain their thinking when they discussed their strategies within their groups and with the whole class. Student page 49 provides additional opportunities for individual assessment.

NCTM Standards Summary

Students used implicit knowledge of certain math properties as they used mental math to solve problems. They recalled basic math facts and tried to do calculations quickly and accurately. They communicated as they worked in groups to devise solution strategies and as they presented their strategies with the class. They extended their understanding by answering general questions about the way algebraic properties work.

Answers

Page 48
Answers may vary. See the lesson for examples.

Page 49
1. Various responses are possible. The friends cannot get box seats, but they can buy any of the other three kinds of seats and still have money left for refreshments.
2. Various responses are possible, but amounts must include $42 for seats.
3. No. Three lower box seats cost $33 and three of each refreshment cost $9.75. If they buy bleacher seats or upper reserved seats the friends would have enough money left to buy 3 juices and 3 hot dogs.
4. The friends would have at least $6.50.

Using Algebraic Properties

**Solve these problems. Use either mental math or estimation.
Record your answer and your strategy.**

Juice		Popcorn		Cereal Bar	
Small	$0.60	Small	$0.75	Small	$ 0.95
Medium	$0.90	Medium	$1.25	Large	$1.25
Large	$1.20	Large	$1.75		

❶ Charlene wants to buy a large juice, a small popcorn, a large cereal bar, and a small juice. How much money does she need?

❷ Shamina wants to buy 3 large popcorns and 2 large cereal bars. How much will she spend?

❸ Nick wants to buy two medium juices for each small cereal bar he buys. He has $8.00. How many juices can he get? What is the total cost of the juices and cereal bars?

❹ Carlos has $8.00. He is with 5 friends. Carlos and his friends each want juice and popcorn. What could Carlos do?

Standard 2 Algebra

Using Algebraic Properties

Use mental math to answer the questions.
Then use words and numbers to explain your method.

Three friends are going to a minor league baseball game. They need to buy tickets.
They want to have some money left over to buy snacks.

Box Seats:	$14.00
Lower Reserved Seats:	$11.00
Upper Reserved Seats:	$9.00
Bleachers:	$6.50

❶ If the friends have $40, what tickets do you think they should buy? Why?

❷ If the friends want to sit in the box seats, how much money would they need?

❸ Hot dogs are $1.75 and juices are $1.50. Could each friend get one hot dog and one juice if they bought lower reserved seats with their $40.00? If not, which seats should they purchase so they still buy a juice and a hot dog?

❹ Toward the end of the game, the friends find they have just enough money left to buy two hot dogs and two juices. About how much money do they have?

Using Expressions

Introduction

Objective → Students will use tables to evaluate variable expressions and identify the value that makes a sentence true.

Context → Students have some experience using variables to represent unknown quantities. They will go on to write and solve equations using inverse operations.

NCTM Standards Focus

In this standards-based lesson, students will make tables to show the value of an expression for different values of a variable. They will then use their tables to identify the value that makes a given sentence true. With this approach, students take the first steps toward understanding the concept of a solution to an equation.

Representation Students will represent relationships using variable expressions and make a table to evaluate a given expression for different values of the variable. The table will provide visual support in identifying the value of the variable that makes a sentence true.

Reasoning and Proof Students will use reasoning to translate a situation into a correct algebraic expression and explain why other expressions do not fit the situation. They will identify patterns in their tables and describe their method for finding a solution from the table.

Connections Writing expressions requires students to use their knowledge of the four arithmetic operations. By using real-life situations, students will recognize how variable expressions provide a convenient shortcut for organizing information.

Teaching Plan

Materials → Student pages 54–55

LEAD OFF THE LESSON by presenting the following situation for students to consider.

> Customers at Video Ranger receive a sale coupon that lets them buy any video for $3 off the regular price.

Ask questions to help students translate the situation into an algebraic expression. *What words describe the price you will pay when you buy a video?* (Regular price minus $3) Explain that this relationship can be shown using a *variable expression.*

In a variable expression, a letter (or symbol) is used to represent a number or quantity whose value can change. Suppose the variable r stands for the regular price of the video. *What expression would represent the sale price?* $(r - 3)$

Record $r - 3$ on the board, labeling r "regular price" and labeling 3 "amount off." Emphasize that the expression $r - 3$ tells the sale price for any regularly priced video.

$$r - 3$$

regular price → ← amount off

- *Could you have used a letter other than* r *to stand for the regular price?* (Yes.)
- *Why is* r *a good choice?* (Since r is the first letter of *regular*, it helps you remember the meaning of the letter.)
- *If the regular price of a video was $10, how would you determine the sale price? Explain.* (Students may either suggest they let r be equal to 10 or they substitute 10 for r so $10 - 3 = 7$.)

Distribute student page 54. Have students work individually to complete the first table to show the sale price for various regular prices. Help them check their work, then have students examine the information in the table.

- *If the regular price is $12, what will the sale price be?* ($9)
- *If the sale price is $8, what was the regular price?* ($11)
- *What patterns do you see in your table?* (As regular price increases, sale price increases; each time the regular price increases by $1, the sale price also increases by $1.)

An *equation* states that two expressions, whether two number expressions, one number and one variable expression, or two variable expressions, have the same value. *Suppose your friend said that she bought a video at a sale price of $15.* We can represent this with the equation $r - 3 = 15$.

ASK STUDENTS TO EXPLAIN how they could use the table to find out the regular price of the video that was purchased for $15. Students should explain they would look in the sale price column until they found $15, and then read across to see what regular price corresponds to that sale price. In this case it is $18.

- *Is there any other regular price for which the sale price is $15?* (No.) Explain that this value for r, $18, is called a *solution* of the sentence $r - 3 = 15$, and the value $18 for r, makes this sentence true.

- *How would you prove that for the sentence* r − 3 = 15, *the value $20 for* r *does not make the sentence true?* (20 − 3 = 17, not 15)

- *Suppose the sentence was* r − 3 = 8. *Explain in words what this sentence means.* (The sale price of some video is $8.)

- *Use your table to find the value of* r *that makes the sentence true.* ($11)

- *Can you find the value of* r *that makes* r − 3 = 25 *true in your table?* (No, there is no sale price of $25 shown.)

- *Explain how you would figure out that value.* (Students might explain that since the sale price of $25 is more than any sale price in their table, they would try regular prices greater than $20. Given a few minutes, most students should discover that a regular price of $28 gives a sale price of $25.)

What Might Happen . . . What to Do

Because the form of the first example, $r − 3 = 15$ is similar to sentences written for basic facts, some students may recognize that the inverse relationship, $15 + 3 = r$, can be used. Tell students that sometimes problems involve more complicated sentences, such as $2r − 3 = 15$, where it is not as easy to identify the inverse relationship or related sentence. However, they will be able to use the table method to find the value of r.

Continue the discussion by presenting another situation. *Mark earns $2 for every hour he does chores around the house. If* h *stands for the number of hours that Mark works, what is the variable expression that tells the amount he will earn?* (2 × h) Explain that this is a multiplication expression in which *h* stands for an unknown number of hours. You might wish to point out the alternative symbolisms for multiplication, 2 · *h*, where the dot is used to avoid confusion between the variable *x* and the × as a times symbol, or simply 2*h*. When a number and variable are together this way, multiplication is known to be the operation.

Have students complete the second table on student page 54 to show how much Mark will earn for different numbers of hours. The simple numbers will ensure that students can complete the table quickly and then focus on using their tables to identify particular values. *How much will Mark earn if he works 3 hours?* ($6)

Challenge students to suggest problems that could be solved by using the second table on student page 54. Also have them tell the sentences that represent their problems. For example, for the problem "*Mark earned $16. How many hours did he work?*," the corresponding sentence is $2h = 16$. Although students may indicate that they know h is 8 by using basic facts, require that they explain the method. Have them use the table to help them with the expressions, as these will gradually become more difficult as they work on the student pages.

Student Pages

Student page 54 includes the tables students will complete during the lesson. Student page 55 provides practice writing and evaluating expressions and identifying solutions to sentences.

Assessment

There were ample opportunities to evaluate students' grasp of the lesson concepts from their participation during the discussion. As students completed tables, you could determine if they understood how to evaluate expressions and identify the value of the variable that makes a given sentence true. Their responses on the student pages make evaluation of their fluency in creating variable expressions possible.

NCTM Standards Summary

Representation was important in this lesson where students made connections between relationships and algebraic expressions. They organized information in tables, creating a visual method for finding solutions for equations. They relied on prior knowledge to choose the operation that represented a given situation, and connected the use of algebraic techniques to real-world problems. Students used reasoning to identify solutions and explained the significance for both the sentences containing the variable, and the solutions. They justified their answers by proving other values did not produce the desired result.

Answers

Page 54
1. 7, 8, 9, 13, 15, 17; $12
2. 4, 6, 10, 16, 20, 28; $h = 32$
3. $\frac{n}{3}$: 1, 2, 4, 5, 6, 8; $\frac{n}{3} + 1$: 2, 3, 5, 6, 7, 9; $n = 18$

Page 55
1. c
2. a
3. 26, 23, 20, 19, 17; $d = 11$
4. 0, 1, 2, 3, 4; $n = 25$
5. 29, 32, 35, 36, 38; $w = 18$

Answers for table: 2, 3, 4, 5, 6
6. $s + 2$
7. $\frac{s + 2}{3}$
8. 13; The table shows $\frac{(s + 2)}{3} = 5$ when $s = 13$
9. $(2 \cdot n) + 4$
10. $n = 23$

Using Expressions

Complete each table and answer the questions.

❶

Regular (r)	Sale price (r − 3)
10	
11	
12	
16	
18	
20	

If the sale price is $15, the regular price is _____.

❷

Hours worked (h)	Amount earned (2 × h)
2	
3	
5	
8	
10	
14	

What value for h makes $2 \times h = 16$ a true sentence?

❸

n	$\frac{n}{3}$	$\left(\frac{n}{3}\right) + 1$
3		
6		
12		
15		
18		
24		

What value for n makes $\frac{n}{3} + 1 = 7$ a true sentence?

Standard 2 Algebra

Using Expressions

Complete each problem.

1 Shari is 10 years old. If y stands for the number of years from now, which expression tells how old Shari will be at that time?

a. $10 - y$ b. $10 \cdot y$ c. $10 + y$ d. $\frac{y}{10}$

2 One pizza serves 6 people. If p stands for the number of pizzas Nick bought for his party, which expression tells how many people were served?

a. $6 \cdot p$ b. $p - 6$ c. $\frac{p}{6}$ d. $p + 6$

Complete each table. Then find the value that makes the sentence true.

3

d	$30 - d$
4	
7	
10	
11	
13	

$$30 - d = 19$$
$$d = \rule{2cm}{0.4pt}$$

4

n	$\frac{n}{5} - 2$
10	
15	
20	
25	
30	

$$\frac{n}{5} - 2 = 3$$
$$n = \rule{2cm}{0.4pt}$$

5

w	$w + 25$
4	
7	
10	
11	
13	

$$w + 25 = 43$$
$$w = \rule{2cm}{0.4pt}$$

Complete the table at the right. Then use the table to answer questions 6–10.

Shells (s)	$\frac{(s + 2)}{3}$
4	
7	
10	
13	
16	

6 Fran had s seashells. She found 2 more shells. Write an expression to show how many shells she had altogether.

7 Fran divided the total number of shells she had among 3 friends. Write an expression to represent what she did.

8 If each of Fran's friends received 5 shells after Fran divided them up, how many shells did Fran have to start with? Explain how you found your answer.

9 Tim is thinking of a number, n. He doubles his number, then adds 4 to it. Write an expression that shows the result.

10 If Tim's result is 50, what was Tim's starting number? Start with 20 and make a table using values of n. Stop when you think you know the answer.

Exploring Ordered Pairs

Introduction

Objective → Students will identify patterns in sets of ordered pairs and find horizontal and vertical distances.

Context → Students have some background graphing and naming ordered pairs in the first quadrant. After studying patterns of points in this restricted region, students will go on to graph ordered pairs in all four quadrants and analyze transformations using coordinates.

NCTM Standards Focus

In this standards-based lesson, students will relate numeric patterns of coordinates to their visual representation. They will analyze patterns by comparing the sets of ordered pairs and their graphs. By emphasizing this approach to graphing throughout the middle-school grades, students will be better prepared for later work with linear and nonlinear relationships.

Representation Students will represent ordered pairs as points on a graph, and they will also represent points as ordered pairs. Students will count spaces to find distances between points and then analyze the ordered pairs represented in tables to find the same distance.

Reasoning and Proof Students will compare and contrast graphs they create from tables. They will analyze the ordered pairs for points on vertical and horizontal lines and will formulate a method for determining the distance between the points. They will use reasoning to identify patterns in sets of ordered pairs and they will predict other ordered pairs that continue the pattern and verify their predictions by graphing.

Communication Throughout the lesson, students will share their understanding and insights. Communication will help to clarify concepts and will provide the motivation for each new idea.

Teaching Plan

Materials → Student pages 60–61; overhead transparency of map (see page 57); grid paper (optional)

To BEGIN THE LESSON, review graphing of ordered pairs. Remind students that an ordered pair identifies the point where two lines intersect; the first number tells the number of units to the right or left of zero, and the second number tells the number of units up or down from zero. Illustrate by placing a point such as (3, 4) on the coordinate graph on the board or overhead.

Distribute student page 60. Direct students' attention to Activity 1. Tell students they will make a town map by graphing and labeling the points for each building listed. Allow students a few minutes to work, then display a transparency of the completed graph. Have students check their graphs against the correct version and make any necessary corrections.

Engage students in a discussion of their graphs.

- *What is the same about the ordered pairs for the park and police station?*
  (The first number is 0.)

- *If the first number of an ordered pair is 0, what can you tell about the location of the point?* (The point is on the vertical number line or *axis*.)

- *If the second number of an ordered pair is 0, what can you tell about the location of the point?* (The point is on the horizontal axis.)

- *Name another ordered pair that would be located on the horizontal axis.*
  [Any point $(a, 0)$]

- *If each space represents 1 block, how far apart are the bank and zoo?*
  (4 blocks) *How did you find your answer?* (Students may suggest they counted spaces.)

- *Do you see another way of finding the distance between the bank and the zoo using their ordered pairs? Explain your thinking.* (Since the bank and zoo are on the same horizontal line, the distance is the difference of the first numbers of their ordered pairs: $8 - 4 = 4$ blocks.)

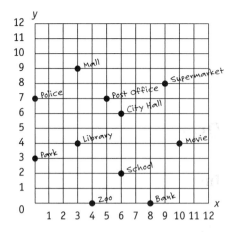

Continue to investigate relationships between the ordered pairs.

- *What is the same about the ordered pairs for the library and movie?*
  (The second number, 4, is the same.)

- *Why are points with the same second number located on a horizontal line?* (The second number tells the number of units up from zero.)

- *Find how far apart the movie and library are. First count spaces, then use their ordered pairs. Explain your method.* (Since the second numbers are the same, subtract the first numbers: $10 - 3 = 7$ blocks.)

NOW DIRECT STUDENTS to look at the points and ordered pairs for City Hall and the school to see what they have in common. Students should articulate that City Hall and the school are on the same vertical line, and that the first numbers of their ordered pairs are the same. Have students find out how far apart City Hall and the school are, first by counting the vertical spaces and then by using their ordered pairs. They should explain that the distance is 4 spaces, and the numbers indicate $6 - 2 = 4$.

Summarize the relationships discovered.

- *When do two ordered pairs represent points on the same horizontal line?*
  (When the second numbers are the same.)

- *How do you find the distance between the points?* (Subtract the smaller x-coordinate from the greater x-coordinate.)

- *When do two ordered pairs represent points on the same vertical line?* (When the x-coordinates are the same.)
- *How do you find the distance between the points?* (Subtract the smaller y-coordinate from the greater y-coordinate.)

Now have students complete the last two items in Activity 1.

NEXT, HAVE STUDENTS FOCUS on Activity 2 in which ordered pairs are represented in tables. Explain to students that the ordered pairs in each table form a pattern. Have them examine the table on the left and describe the rule that tells how to find the second number, given the first. Most students should be able to identify that the first number is doubled to get the second number. Write the rule for this table on the board.

second number = 2 × first number

Have students graph the ordered pairs in the table on the first grid and then describe the points on their graphs. They should suggest that the points seem to be along a straight line and are evenly spaced.

- *If you had made a mistake filling in the table, how would the graph show your mistake?* (The point would not be along the same line as the others.)
- *Start at the first point that represents the ordered pair (0, 0). Explain how to move to get to the next point.* (Across 1, up 2) *To the next point?* (Across 1, up 2)
- *Will the moves always be the same from one point to the next?* (Yes.)

Have students examine the second table. Ask them to describe the rule that tells how to find the second number, given the first number. Most students will recognize that the second number is 1 more than the first number. Write the rule on the board.

second number = first number + 1

Direct students to graph all the points on the second grid. When they are finished, ask them to describe their graphs. Students should observe the linear pattern and spacing of the points. Have them explain the movement from one point to the next on this graph. (Right 1, up 1) *How is the movement on this graph different than on the first graph?* (On the first graph, you moved 1 right, and 2 up; on this graph you move 1 right and 1 up.) Help students compare and contrast the appearance of the two graphs.

Students should observe that the set of points on the first graph goes up more sharply and that the points on the first graph seem "farther apart."

IF TIME PERMITS, you may wish to have students work individually or in small groups to create other examples of tables of ordered pairs that follow a rule. Students should provide space in their tables for missing numbers. They can exchange papers, complete each other's tables, and graph the ordered pairs. (Extra grid paper will be required for this optional activity.) Students should share their graphs as a class and make comparisons about the point-to-point movements for the ordered pairs. As students observe a variety of examples, they will develop insight into the relationships among the rule, the movements, and the appearance of the graph.

Student Pages

Student page 60 includes questions and organized recording space for Activities 1 and 2. Student page 61 provides additional practice graphing ordered pairs, finding distances, and identifying patterns.

Assessment

As students worked on their town maps, you were able to assess their proficiency in graphing ordered pairs, identifying points, and finding horizontal and vertical distances. Students' responses during the discussion of tables of ordered pairs allowed you to note and evaluate their understanding of rules and movements from point-to-point.

NCTM Standards Summary

As students represented ordered pairs as points on a graph, they identified horizontal and vertical relationships and formulated a method for finding distances. Identifying patterns in tables of ordered pairs and comparing their findings with their graphs enabled students to draw conclusions about the appearance of the graphs. The emphasis on communication throughout the lesson made it possible for a variety of ideas to be explored. This approach helped show relationships rather than making graphing a mechanical skill.

Answers

Page 60

Activity 1
1. Check students' graphs.
2. Bank and zoo, 4 spaces;
   $(8, 0)$, $(4, 0)$; $8 - 4 = 4$
   Movie and library, 7 spaces;
   $(10, 4)$, $(3, 4)$; $10 - 3 = 7$
   City Hall and school, 4 spaces;
   $(6, 6)$, $(6, 2)$; $6 - 2 = 4$
   Post Office and police station,
   5 spaces; $(5, 7)$, $(0, 7)$; $5 - 0 = 5$

Activity 2
Check students' graphs.

Page 61

1–8. Check students' graphs.
9. $6 - 2 = 4$
10. $6 - 2 = 4$
11. G and B are closer; G and B are three units apart, F and B are 5 units apart.
12. $(1, 1)$
13. Rule: second number = first number + 2; check students' graphs.
14. Rule: second number $= \frac{1}{2}$ first number *or* first number increases by 1, second number increases by $\frac{1}{2}$.
15. Ordered pairs will vary; Rule: second number $= 3 \times$ first number + 1 *or* first number increases by 1, second number increases by 3.
16. Pattern: first number increases by 3, second number increases by 2; $(9, 7)$ does not fit; the correct point is $(10, 8)$.

Exploring Ordered Pairs

Activity 1
Graph the ordered pairs. Label each location.

❶

(6, 6)	City Hall	(0, 7)	Police Station
(3, 4)	Library	(3, 9)	Mall
(6, 2)	School	(5, 7)	Post Office
(4, 0)	Zoo	(0, 3)	Park
(9, 8)	Supermarket	(8, 0)	Bank
(10, 4)	Movie		

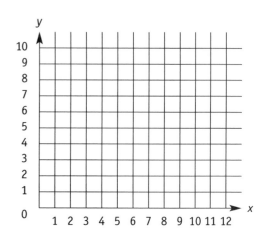

Find the distance between each set of locations.
First count spaces. Then write the ordered pairs and show how to subtract.

❷

Locations	Spaces	Ordered Pairs	Subtraction
Bank and Zoo			
Movie and Library			
City Hall and School			
Post Office and Police Station			

Activity 2
Graph the ordered pairs.

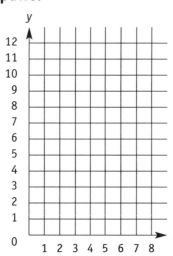

(x) First Number	(y) Second Number
0	0
1	2
2	4
3	6
4	8
5	10
6	12

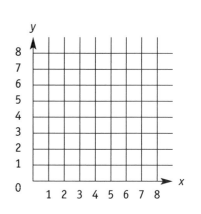

(x) First Number	(y) Second Number
0	1
1	2
2	3
3	4
4	5
5	6
6	7

Standard 2 Algebra

Exploring Ordered Pairs

Graph the ordered pairs. Label the points.

❶ $A = (0, 2)$ **❷** $B = (4, 3)$ **❸** $C = (2, 5)$ **❹** $D = (0, 6)$

❺ $E = (6, 5)$ **❻** $F = (4, 8)$ **❼** $G = (7, 3)$ **❽** $H = (8, 1)$

Locate the following points on your graph. Find the distance between the two points by subtracting. Check by counting spaces.

❾ D and A **❿** E and C

⓫ Which two points are closer together, F and B or G and B? Explain.

⓬ Draw point J on the graph so that it is on the same horizontal line as H and 7 units away from H. Write the ordered pair for J.

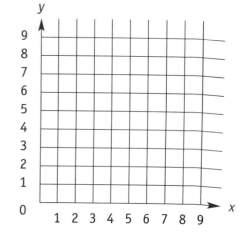

For questions 13 and 14, give the rule for finding the second number from the first number. Complete the table and place the ordered pairs on the graph.

⓭

(x) First Number	(y) Second Number
0	2
1	3
2	4
3	5
4	6
5	7
6	8

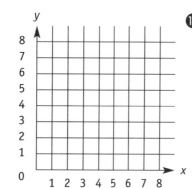

Rule: _____

⓮

(x) First Number	(y) Second Number
0	0
1	$\frac{1}{2}$
2	1
3	$1\frac{1}{2}$
4	2
5	$2\frac{1}{2}$
6	3

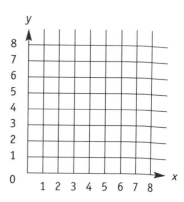

Rule: _____

⓯ Write four other ordered pairs that fit this pattern: (0, 1), (1, 4), (2, 7), (3, 10). What rule did you use?

⓰ Challenge All but one of these ordered pairs fit a pattern: (1, 2), (4, 4), (7, 6), (9, 7), (13, 10), (16, 12). Which pair does not fit the pattern? Explain why and give the correct ordered pair. (Graphing the points may help you find the pattern.)

Exploring Inverses: Addition and Subtraction

Introduction

Objective → Students will relate addition and subtraction as inverse operations to solve equations.

Context → This lesson comes after students have had limited experience with variables and equations. The lesson prepares students for more work with variables, solving simple equations, and the idea of functions.

Exploring Inverses: Addition and Subtraction
....

Learn

Robert has a computer program that performs different operations on numbers that are input. One operation adds 5 to the input number.

Operation: Add 5

Input	16	17	18	19	20	21
Result	21	22	23	24	25	26

What would the result be if you input 213?

Robert does not remember what another operation of the program does. If he inputs 48 and the result is 71, can you find the operation?

$48 + n = 71$ n stands for the missing number

You can solve this addition problem by writing a related subtraction problem.

$71 - 48 = n$, so $n = 23$

and

$48 + 23 = 71$

The operation is add 23.

You can use subtraction to find a missing addend because addition and subtraction are **inverse operations**.

Try

Find n in each sentence.

1. $12 + n = 27$ **2.** $21 - n = 13$ **3.** $n + 323 = 412$ **4.** $n - 204 = 397$

NCTM Process Standards Analysis and Focus

The standards analysis examines how the process standards have been incorporated into the above lesson. By increasing the focus on three of the process standards, a more effective and meaningful lesson can be presented. The suggestions offered can help you to think about how this might be accomplished.

Reasoning and Proof The lesson asks students to determine rules that describe functions. While reasoning is involved to identify rules, students are not asked to generalize information that will help them find a missing term in a sentence that is not part of a function.

Suggestion → Have students use reasoning to solve equations and then explain their methods. Creating their own solution methods will result in

Explore

Write a subtraction sentence for $\diamondsuit + \square = \triangle$. Share your ideas.

Practice

Find n.

5. $n + 24 = 46$ **6.** $17 + n = 91$ **7.** $53 - n = 12$ **8.** $109 + n = 161$

9. $n - 83 = 112$ **10.** $77 - n = 32$ **11.** $802 + n = 966$ **12.** $n - 17 = 96$

13. $23 + n = 62$ **14.** $n + 106 = 205$ **15.** $n - 32 = 133$ **16.** $189 - n = 126$

Do the operation indicated to find each result.

17. Operation: Add 15

Input	25	30	35	40	45
Result					

18. Operation: Subtract 7

Input	17	12	45	132	21
Result					

19. Operation: Subtract 21

Input	42	48	58	62	78
Result					

20. Operation: Add 19

Input	8	11	21	31	41
Result					

21. Find the operation.

Input	12	23	34	45	56
Result	21	32	43	54	65

22. Find the operation.

Input	19	43	52	36	28
Result	2	26	35	19	11

Problem Solving

Play Mystery Number with a partner.
Each player writes an addition problem. The sum cannot be greater than 99.
Rewrite the problem leaving out one of the addends. Exchange problems and solve.
Write a subtraction problem for the next game.

establishing procedures that are meaningful to students. Have students prove their solutions by substituting their answers into the original equations.

Connections The lesson tells students that addition and subtraction are inverse operations but does not provide information that helps students generalize this information so they can apply it to solving equations.

Suggestion → Have students refer to prior knowledge of related addition and subtraction sentences to reinforce that the two operations are inverses. This will help students see how solving equations is related to information they already know.

Representation Analyzing functions is introduced as a mechanism to find a missing term; although this identifies a term that establishes a rule, it is not helpful in solving individual equations.

Suggestion → Focus students' attention on the equation form and what the variable represents in an equation. Have students use manipulatives to create visual models that reinforce the inverse relationship between addition and subtraction.

Communication While opportunities for communication are limited, a thoughtful exercise presents an addition sentence and asks students to write a related subtraction sentence.

Problem Solving Problem solving consists of a game children can play to find a missing addend when the sum and other addend are given.

The teaching plan that follows shows how the suggestions for increasing the focus on the process standards can be implemented.

Revised Teaching Plan

Materials → 40 counters for each pair of students (optional)

BEGIN THE LESSON BY HAVING STUDENTS tap into their prior knowledge about number sentences. Write $2 + 5 = 7$ on the board, and ask students: *How would you read this number sentence aloud?* Directly underneath, write $n + 5 = 7$, and ask the same question. Remind students that the letter in a number sentence is called a variable and that it represents any number that will make the sentence true. *Until we know what number it stands for, we just say the letter. How would we say this number sentence?* (n plus five equals seven.)

Tell students that when we are trying to find out what number is represented by a variable, it helps to substitute *what number* for the letter. Thus the number sentence could also be read "What number plus five equals seven?" *What number is* n *equal to in this sentence?* (2) *How do you know?* Beyond the give-away of writing it just below $2 + 5 = 7$, ask students if there are other ways they could find out what number added to 5 equals 7.

You may wish to model the relationships with counters on the overhead to reinforce this abstraction visually. *You know you'll need to have a total of 7. Here are 7 counters, and you already have 5* (moving those aside). *How many more do you need to get 7?* (2 counters are left.) *So what does* n *stand for?*

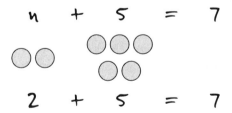

PRESENT PAIRS OF EQUATIONS for students to solve. Pair a simple problem such as $n + 14 = 37$ with a less obvious problem like $n + 127 = 253$. Have students work with a partner to determine the value represented by the variable in each equation. Instruct students to record the steps they use as they solve each problem. Monitor students as they work together. Encourage them to look for connections between the two problems. *Were the steps you did for* n + 14 = 37 *the same or different from the steps you needed to solve* n + 127 = 253?

Engage students in a whole-group discussion so that they can share and compare results and methods. Encourage reticent students to share their notes from the activity. Summarize the various methods on the board.

Remind students that although there are many methods for solving a problem, the goal is to find a method that will always work with a similar type of problem. Help students generalize. *Would your method work with any numbers? How do you know?* If no one has mentioned using the related subtraction fact, 253 − 127 = 126, introduce this as a way to the find the missing term. *Would using a related subtraction sentence like this work? Can you subtract the number you're adding to* n *from the total to find out what* n *must be? If* n + 127 = 253, *does* 253 − 127 = n?

What Might Happen . . . What to Do

Two important concepts in algebra—variables and equality—are fundamental to students' understanding and ability to reason in this lesson. To help students begin thinking algebraically, review fact families and substitute a variable for one of the numbers in the fact. If students can make connections between $2 + 7 = 9$, $2 + n = 9$, $9 = 2 + 7$, and $9 = 2 + n$, they will be well on their way to an understanding of basic algebra.

PRESENT AN ADDITION EQUATION such as $n + 14 = 76$. *Would the answer be different if it were written* 14 + n = 76? Having students compare these two different formats makes clear that solving addition sentences can easily be accomplished by using subtraction. Representing the relationships with related fact family sentences helps to reinforce those fact relationships.

Next, have students look at a subtraction equation such as $n - 24 = 38$. Ask partners to solve this equation for *n* and again record their method. Some

© Creative Publications

f.y.i.

While using inverse operations works to solve many equations, it doesn't automatically apply. Because addition is commutative, using the inverse operation will work regardless of the order of the addends. However, since subtraction is not commutative, changing $146 - n = 93$ to $n - 146 = 93$ results in a different problem. In many subtraction problems, the numbers on either side of the equal sign can be added together to give the number being subtracted from, but if one of those numbers is a variable, we don't have two numbers to add together. You may want to discuss problems of this type in another class period, since a more in-depth investigation of this type of equation would be worthwhile to help students solidify their understanding.

coaching may be helpful. *What number minus 24 equals 38?* Calling attention to the relative sizes of the numbers may also be helpful. *Will* n *be larger or smaller than 24 if you take 24 away from it and are left with 38?* Students should now have at least an informal understanding that they can use the related addition sentence $n = 24 + 38$ to solve this problem.

At this point, students should see that each of the above equations can be solved using the opposite or inverse operation. Remind students that subtraction takes apart what addition puts together. Addition puts together what subtraction has taken apart. Consider modeling these concepts with simple problems and counters on the overhead to reinforce understanding.

Write $146 - n = 93$ on the board. Ask students how they would express this number sentence in words. (146 minus *n equals* 93, or 146 minus *what number* equals 93.) Tell partners to solve this equation and discuss their procedures. Students will find that this equation does not immediately lend itself to using inverse operations. You cannot add 93 and 146 together to find *n*. It's important that students see the necessity of thinking problems through rather than merely applying a rule. Help them see that instead of using addition here, using the related subtraction fact will help them find the missing term. Show a pair of simpler equations such as $5 - n = 3$ and $5 - 3 = n$. If appropriate, model this simpler problem with the counters on the overhead.

CONCLUDE THE LESSON by asking students to summarize the procedures they defined for solving equations. *Can the same method be used to solve for* n *in both* n + 14 = 78 *and* 14 + n = 78? *What is the method? Can the same method be used to solve* 48 − n = 13 *and* n − 5 = 6? *What is the method?*

In the first problem, students should understand that subtracting the 14 that has been added to *n* in either sentence isolates the variable. Since addition is commutative, the order of the addends does not interfere with undoing the addition with subtraction. In the second problem, $n - 5 = 6$, students should be able to see that addition can be used to find *n* because putting the amount being subtracted together with the remainder gives what was started out with. For $48 - n = 13$, however, addition is not helpful because we don't know what to add to the 13. However, knowing the related subtraction fact can help solve this equation.

Student Pages

Students should now be ready to complete exercises similar to those on the reduced student pages. Remind students to look for opportunities to use the relationship between addition and subtraction to solve the equations.

Assessment

As students worked though the problems in the lesson, you could assess whether or not they applied reasoning and made an active attempt to solve the equations. Discussions and responses to questions provided opportunities to determine whether students successfully made the connection between addition and subtraction as inverse operations and understood how to use related math sentences to solve equations.

NCTM Standards Summary

In this lesson, making connections to prior knowledge of the relationship between addition and subtraction laid a foundation to develop sound algebraic thinking. Students applied reasoning as they examined various addition and subtraction equations to determine the value represented by the variable. After solving addition and subtraction equations, they generalized their methods. Manipulatives were used to model the connection between addition and subtraction and reinforce their inverse relationship. These activities opened up opportunities for students to share their ideas and explain their methods, reinforcing their understanding of the role inverse operations and related math sentences play in solving equations.

Standard 3 **Geometry**

AT THE FIFTH GRADE LEVEL, geometry includes work with congruence and similarity, representing three-dimensional shapes, transformations, and circles. Our lessons are derived from these important topics. They include a lesson on understanding similarity, a lesson on understanding transformations, a lesson on investigating nets, and a lesson on circumference and diameter.

Three lessons model how the process standards can be used to teach content. A fourth lesson is a hypothetical textbook lesson that we have revised to be more standards based. These four lessons do not represent the entire curriculum, but rather provide glimpses of how, with a more concentrated effort to incorporate the process standards, better mathematics teaching and learning can be achieved.

In one lesson we have chosen, students will understand how to create similar figures using transformations and proportional reasoning. This lesson is generally given superficial treatment at this level. Through the process standards of reasoning and proof, problem solving, and connections, students are presented a concrete exploration and analysis of what makes figures similar.

Another lesson we have chosen explores the slide transformation on a coordinate graph. Through the process standards of reasoning and proof, communication, and connections, students will understand the slide transformation, both geometrically and mathematically, by examining the coordinates of the vertices of a rectangle on a plane.

A third lesson we have chosen has students experimenting with making nets for three-dimensional shapes. By incorporating the process standards of reasoning and proof, representation, and connections, students realize that nets are two-dimensional representations of three-dimensional figures. They use reasoning and experimentation to determine whether or not a given net is of a particular shape.

The hypothetical textbook lesson we have chosen to revise is one that explores the circumference and diameter of a circle. Through better incorporation of the process standards of problem solving, reasoning and proof, and communication, students will discover for themselves, rather than being told, the relationship between circumference and diameter.

Standard 3 Lessons

Understanding Similarity

Understanding Transformations

Investigating Nets

Exploring Circumference and Diameter

Understanding Similarity

Introduction

Objective → Students will be able to understand how to create similar figures by using transformations and proportional reasoning.

Context → Students have worked with two-dimensional shapes on many different levels. They have explored their various dimensions, angle measures, areas, and perimeters. They have also worked with flips and rotations, and have explored the concept of congruence. Students are ready to learn about the concept of similarity as it relates to some very basic regular geometric shapes.

NCTM Standards Focus

The concept of similarity is one that traditionally receives a light touch in fifth-grade classrooms. This is usually limited to one or two examples and a series of exercises for students to complete by referring to the examples. Students who understand the examples may complete the exercises flawlessly, yet are rarely able to apply their "learning" to similar situations they encounter later. This can be attributed to the lack of concrete exploration and analysis of what makes figures similar. In this standards-based lesson, students look critically at similar figures and break them down in order to identify their corresponding parts.

Reasoning and Proof Students look closely at three rectangles on the coordinate plane. They identify characteristics of the rectangles that are alike and ones that are different. They apply reasoning skills to determine which of the rectangles are similar, and they are able to provide concrete proof to support their selections.

Problem Solving Students apply problem-solving skills when looking critically at the rectangles presented to them. They break the rectangles down into smaller chunks by recording their attributes in an organized table. This allows students to see patterns and relationships that can then be applied to verify the similarity of figures they later construct on their own.

Connections Students are able to relate the ideas of similarity to their understanding of proportionality and transformations. They work with rectangles to explore the concept of similarity with nothing more than a sheet of blank grid paper. This follows an initial analysis of the rectangles provided, where students chart attributes (length, width, angle measures) and the ordered pairs that name the corners. Doing so allows students to identify patterns which are then connected to figures they construct on their own.

Teaching Plan

Materials → Student pages 74–75; 1-cm grid paper; rulers

TELL STUDENTS THAT TODAY they are going to focus on the topic of similarity. Briefly discuss what the word *similar* means to them in their daily lives. Pass out student page 74, and ask students to look at the rectangles. Have them work in small groups or with partners to list how the rectangles are alike and different. Bring the whole class back together, and let groups share their results. Discuss the word *similar* as it arises. If no one has used the word *similar*, use it now. Ask if any pair of rectangles seem to have a more similar shape than the other one. Tell the class that *similarity* is a mathematical term used to describe shapes that meet certain conditions. Their job today will be to identify and be able to apply two of these conditions.

Pass out a copy of student page 75 to each student. Point out that the two rectangles that were alike on the previous page are also located on this page. *What's different about the placement of these rectangles?* They should quickly notice that all four of the rectangles have their lower-left corner at the same starting point, the origin of the coordinate grid.

DIRECT STUDENTS' ATTENTION to the tables below the grid. Point out that they are to record the *length, width,* and *angle measures* for each of the rectangles. Also, they are to record the *x*- and *y*-coordinates for all four corners of each rectangle. Tell students that, when recording information in both tables, they should begin looking for patterns that may help prove why these rectangles are similar.

Have students work in their same groups. Encourage students to discuss their ideas and reasoning before recording information. Once students have finished, have them report back to the class. You may want to make a transparency of page 75 and record the data provided by students. Should any discrepancies arise, have groups that disagree explain their reasoning. This discussion will allow students to discover their own errors and to reach a consensus with the class. While students are presenting, you may want to pose some questions:

- *What pattern do you see in the length/width of the rectangles?*
- *What patterns do you see in the x- and y-coordinates of the corners?*
- *Do you see any relationships between the patterns in the length/width and the x- and y-coordinates of the corners? If so, what are they?*
- *What role do you think that angle measures play in determining whether or not figures are similar? What about side measures?*

f.y.i.

Some students may have a difficult time seeing how the two rectangles at the top of page 74 are alike because of their positioning. If this is the case, connect this to their learning of transformations. Have students recreate the rectangle in the upper-right corner by rotating it 90°. This should help them to see a more distinct relationship between the two rectangles.

f.y.i.

Students should have pointed out that the angle measures in the previous examples were all identical and that the same is true in this case.

Through their reporting and discussion of these questions, students should begin to notice the following:

- They should identify that the length increases by 3 units each time, and that the corresponding width increases by 2 units.

- They should notice that the length measurements are also represented by the x-coordinate for the lower-right corner of all four rectangles, and that the width measurements are also represented by the y-coordinate of the upper-left corner of all four rectangles.

Ask students to determine the ratio of the length to the width and the x- and y-coordinates of the upper-right corners of all four rectangles. They should see the relationship between these two sets of numbers. Point out that one method of determining whether figures are similar is to see if their measurements form equal ratios. Write the following on the board or overhead:

$$\frac{3}{2} = \frac{6}{4} = \frac{9}{6} = \frac{12}{8}$$

Point out that these measurements all represent equal ratios. This is one of the conditions that determines the similarity of figures. Have students refer back to student page 74 and look at the rectangle at the bottom of the page and the one on the top left. Write the following on the board or overhead:

$$\frac{3}{2} = \frac{9}{3}$$

Is this equation true? Students should see that these are not equal ratios. Analyzing the equation will help students solidify their understanding of one condition for determining similarity. Inform students that another condition is that the figures are of the same shape, a condition shared with the concept of *congruency*. *If similar figures must be the same shape, what does that say about the angle measures of similar figures?* Students should note that for all similar figures, corresponding angle measures must be congruent. In the case of the rectangles, where all angle measures are 90°, this was easy to see.

PASS GRID PAPER OUT TO STUDENTS. Tell them that their group is to make two rectangles that are not similar. They are going to give those rectangles to another group. That group's goal is to make a similar rectangle for each rectangle. They are also to write a short description of how they made the similar rectangles.

Bring the groups back together to share their results. When they have finished, have the class write a general description of making a rectangle similar to another rectangle. Doing so will help them both in their understanding of similarity and in the development of their reasoning skills. Finish the lesson with a review of similar figures. For homework, consider asking individuals to make three different groups of similar rectangles with three rectangles in each group.

Student Pages

Student page 74 shows a coordinate grid with three rectangles for use in class. Student page 75 shows four similar rectangles on a coordinate grid, all with the lower-left corner at (0, 0). Below the grid there are two tables for students to complete.

Assessment

While students looked at the rectangles presented on the student pages, you were able to assess their ability to identify how the shapes were alike and how they were different. You then observed how students could identify patterns in the results that would support the notion that the figures were indeed similar. When constructing similar rectangles on their own, you assessed whether or not students understood similarity enough to create their own similar figures.

NCTM Standards Summary

In this lesson, students looked at three different rectangles to determine what made them alike and what made them different. They employed problem-solving skills as two of the rectangles were similar but in different positions. Students then looked at a new series of rectangles that were all similar. They identified patterns that helped them both reason and prove that the rectangles were indeed similar. They then connected this learning to a situation where they constructed similar rectangles.

Answers

Page 74
Student responses will vary.

Page 75
Rectangle A: 3, 2, 90°
Rectangle B: 6, 4, 90°
Rectangle C: 9, 6, 90°
Rectangle D: 12, 8, 90°

Rectangle A:
(0, 0); (3,0); (0, 2); (3, 2)
Rectangle B:
(0, 0); (6, 0); (0, 4); (6, 4)
Rectangle C:
(0, 0); (9, 0); (0, 6); (9, 6)
Rectangle D:
(0, 0); (12, 0); (0, 8); (12, 8)

Understanding Similarity

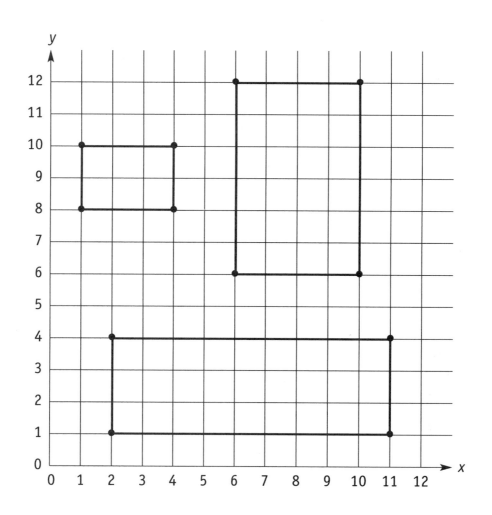

List how the figures above are alike and how they are different.

Alike   Different

_____   _____

_____   _____

_____   _____

_____   _____

_____   _____

Standard 3 Geometry

Understanding Similarity

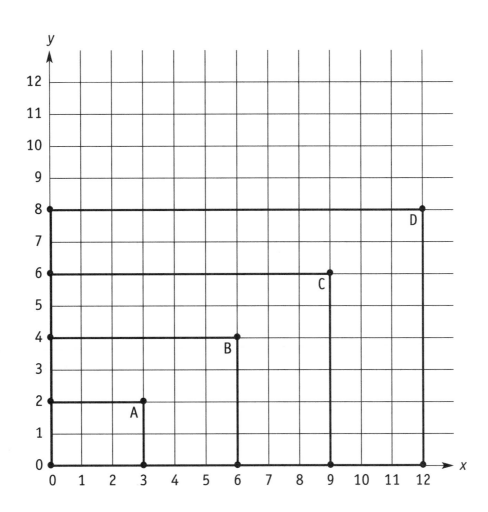

Refer to the rectangles above to complete the tables.
Look for patterns that show these rectangles are similar.

Rectangle	Length (in units)	Width (in units)	Angle Measures
A			
B			
C			
D			

Rectangle	Lower Left	Lower Right	Upper Left	Upper Right
A				
B				
C				
D				

NCTM Standards Focus

A prime objective in the geometry strand in the intermediate years is to understand the characteristics of two-dimensional objects and the concept of transformations. This lesson gives students opportunities to perform hands-on slides on a coordinate grid and to understand the transformations mathematically through an analysis of how the x- and y-values of the vertices of a figure are changed by the slide.

Reasoning and Proof Students will slide figures on a coordinate grid and use the results to reason about the properties of the figures. Students will also make predictions about the outcomes of certain slides.

Communication Students will share ideas about how slides work, how the coordinates of rectangles change during slides, and how to predict changes.

Connections Students will make connections to their previous work with the coordinate graph system.

Teaching Plan

Materials → Student pages 80–81; graph paper (2 pieces per student); straightedge; scissors

BEGIN THE LESSON by telling students that, in this lesson, they will be working with all four quadrants. Tell them they will be placing a figure on the plane and sliding it a certain number of spaces in one or more directions. They will predict what the vertices of the figure will be after the slide occurs.

Pass out several sheets of graph paper to each student or pair of students. Have them draw a coordinate plane. The axes should extend at least 12 units in each of the four directions. Take a few moments to call out the coordinates of some points and ask students to locate the points and tell which quadrant they are in. You may want students to label the quadrants.

NOW HAVE STUDENTS use graph paper to cut out a rectangle that is 4 units by 2 units. Several students can use one sheet of graph paper to conserve paper. Tell students to place their rectangles on their coordinate grids so that one vertex is at (2, 6), and another is at (4, 2). Ask them where the other two vertices are [(2, 2) and (4, 6)]. Now have them trace the rectangle

Understanding Transformations

Introduction

Objective → Students will be able to predict the outcome of slides.

Context → Students have graphed in all four quadrants. They have worked with slides, flips and turns of figures in open spaces. In this lesson they slide figures in all four quadrants, both predicting and recording their moves. This lesson comes toward the end of the year. Next year students will look at both turning and flipping figures in all four quadrants.

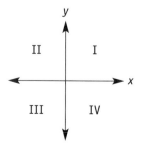

and label it *A*. Discuss the position of the rectangle on the grid using the following questions.

- *What do you notice about the coordinates of the corners/vertices? Are some of the numbers the same?* (Yes, each vertex shares one coordinate with two of the other vertices.)
- *What corners/vertices don't share any coordinates?* (Ones that are located diagonally from each other)
- *What would happen to the coordinates if the rectangle were moved?* (The coordinates would change.)
- *Would all the coordinates change?* (Gather a few responses for this question, but do not label any of the answers correct or incorrect. This point will be covered in the next portion of the lesson.)

f.y.i.

Make sure students have graph paper for sketching their rectangles before and after sliding them.

GIVE EACH STUDENT SEVERAL COPIES of student page 80 to use as a recording sheet. Tell students that you will give them directions for sliding their rectangles. Also tell students that they will use page 80 to record information about the location of the rectangle before and after the slide. They will also use page 80 to record their predictions about the location of the rectangle after the slide. Explain to students that they will be using graph paper to sketch the location of their rectangles before and after the slides.

Tell students that the direction for the first slide is *down 8 spaces.* (You may want to call this Slide B.) Before they make the slide, have students sketch the rectangle in its starting place. Then have students use page 80 to record the starting coordinates of the vertices [(2, 6), (4, 2), (2, 2), (4, 6)], the starting quadrant (I), the directions for the slide, and their predictions about the location of the rectangle after the slide.

Take time to let students discuss the reasoning they used to make their predictions. Tell them that they will be making several more slides, so they will get a chance to test their strategies for making predictions with other slides.

Now have them make the slide, sketch the rectangle in its new position, and fill in the rest of their recording sheet. Discuss the slide with the students. *What are the new coordinates?* [(2, −6), (4, −6), (2, −2), and (4, −2)] *What quadrant is the rectangle in now?* (IV)

What happened to the x-coordinates? (They did not change.) *Why not?*
What happened to the y-coordinates? (They changed by 8.) *Why?*
Was your prediction correct? Will you do anything differently next time?

Take some time to discuss students' predictions. Allow students to comment on each other's methods and ask questions about them. Record some of their methods on the board so students can try the methods in situations to come.

What Might Happen . . . What to Do

Some students might have difficulty moving from the positive side of an axis to the negative side. If the x coordinate is 2, and they need to move 8 down, help them | by breaking down the move into two parts. First move to 0 (that is a move of 2), and then ask them how many they have to move to finally move 8. (6 more)

NOW HAVE STUDENTS return their rectangles to their original position. Tell students to slide their rectangles 7 spaces to the left. (You may want to call this Slide C.) Have them predict, sketch, and record as before. Use the same questions to discuss what they did.

The new rectangle will be in quadrant II and will have the coordinates $(-5, 2)$, $(-3, 2)$, $(-5, 6)$, and $(-3, 6)$. The major difference between this slide and the previous one is that the *y*-coordinates did not change. Again, discuss students' methods for making predictions and ask if anyone made any changes or refinements and why.

Have students return the rectangles to their original location on the coordinate plane [$(2, 6)$, $(4, 2)$, $(2, 2)$, $(4, 6)$]. Tell them that for the next slide—you may want to call this Slide D—you want to give directions that will put the rectangle in quadrant III. Ask for suggestions. *Will moving the rectangle down be enough?* (No.) *Will moving the rectangle left be enough?* (No.) Lead students to see that the rectangle will need to be moved both down and to the left. Tell students to slide their rectangles *down 8 and left 7.* After students have completed the slide, and sketched and recorded the coordinates of the vertices, discuss the results. You may want to use the same set of questions you used for previous slides.

Conclude the lesson by discussing with students how they can predict the results of a slide on a coordinate grid.

What Students Might Say

- When a figure slides only up or down, the x-coordinates remain the same, but the y-coordinates change.

- When a figure slides only to the right or to the left, the y-coordinates remain the same, but the x-coordinates change.

- When a figure slides in more than one direction both the x- and y-coordinates change.

Assign student page 81 either as class work or homework.

Student Pages

Student page 80 is a recording sheet. Student page 81 contains problems similar to the ones done in the class activity.

Assessment

You had opportunities to assess students' understanding of coordinate geometry as they located points when given x- and y-coordinates and as they used coordinates to name points on the coordinate plane. You were able to assess their ability to execute slides and to name the coordinates of vertices before and after slides occurred. You were able to assess their reasoning skills as students made and explained their predictions.

NCTM Standards Summary

Students connected to their prior knowledge as they created a coordinate plane and reviewed how to plot points on it. They extended their understanding as they made connections between coordinate and transformational geometry, first making simple slides along the x- or y-axis, and then by making more complex slides requiring movement along both axes. In each case, they used reasoning as they predicted the location of a figure after a slide.

f.y.i.

Students may realize this slide is a combination of the two slides they did previously. They can make a prediction by using the y-coordinates from the first slide (B) and the x-coordinates from the second slide (C).

Answers

Page 80
See text for answers.

Page 81
1. 6 by 3
2. (1, 4)
3. (0, 1), (4, 11), and (4, 6)
4. 1 to the right, 4 down

Understanding Transformations

Use this page for the class activity.

Slide _____

❶ What are the starting coordinates of the vertices of the rectangle?

❷ What is the starting quadrant?

❸ What are the directions for the slide?

❹ What do you predict the coordinates of the vertices will be after the slide?

❺ What quadrant do you predict the rectangle will be in after the slide?

❻ What are the coordinates of the vertices of your rectangle after the slide?

❼ What quadrant is the rectangle in after the slide?

Standard 3 Geometry

Understanding Transformations

Use the coordinate plane to answer the questions.

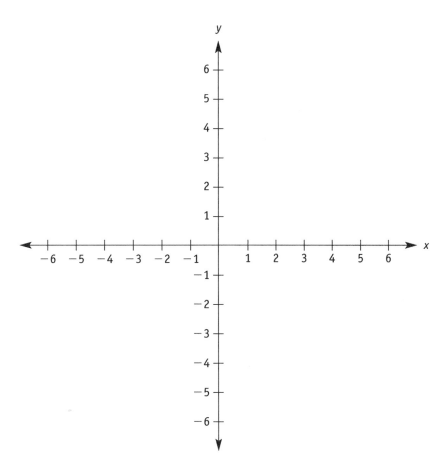

① Imagine a rectangle with two of its vertices at (5, 2) and (−1, −1). What are the dimensions of this rectangle?

② One of the vertices of a rectangle is at (−4, −2). The rectangle slides 5 to the right and 6 up. What are the coordinates of the vertex after the slide?

③ The vertices of a triangle are (−4, −5), (0, −5), and (0, 0). The triangle slides 4 to the right and 6 up. What are the coordinates of the vertices after the slide?

④ The vertices of a square were at (−6, 6), (−2, 6), (−6, 2) and (−2, 2). After a slide, the vertices are (−5, 2), (−1, 2), (−5, −2), and (−1, −2). Describe the slide.

Standard 3 Geometry

Investigating Nets

Introduction

Objective → Students will make a net of a cube and learn how to identify whether or not a net is valid for a particular figure.

Context → Students have studied both two-dimensional and three-dimensional shapes. They have an understanding of the relationship between two-dimensional and three-dimensional shapes. While students may have seen nets in earlier grades, this is the first formal lesson on making nets. Future lessons at this grade will focus on surface area and volume.

NCTM Standards Focus

Spatial reasoning is an important component of the standards. Working with nets, in this lesson students will be connecting two-dimensional and three-dimensional geometry in a very hands-on way. The approach used in this lesson is one that has students develop an understanding of nets as they attempt to make one for a cube. Students reason and communicate as they solve the problem of constructing the net.

Reasoning and Proof Students will look at three-dimensional objects; analyze their faces, edges, and vertices; and predict whether specific nets can be folded to completely cover the shapes. There is an emphasis in the lesson on students explaining the strategies they used.

Representation In constructing the nets, students will work with the actual three-dimensional object. They will use both reasoning and experimentation to confirm whether or not a net works. The goal of the lesson is to enable students to look at the net representation of the three-dimensional object and work toward seeing if the net works without having to try it.

Connections At the heart of this lesson is the connection between a two-dimensional shape and a three-dimensional shape. Students use their reasoning skills to become more proficient at making these connections.

Teaching Plan

Materials → Student pages 86–87; a cube (about 2 inches by 2 inches by 2 inches) for each group of students; paper for making nets; rulers

Preparation → Before class begins, prepare a net for one of the cubes.

TELL STUDENTS THAT IN THIS LESSON they will be learning how to make nets and how to tell if a drawing is a net for a given shape. Show the class the cube covered with the net. Ask the class how they might cover this cube exactly with no extra paper. Some students might suggest cutting out individual two-dimensional figures for each shape. If they do, tell them that they have to cover the cube using only one continuous section of paper. Uncover your cube and tell them that what you are talking about is a net and that this is an example of one. Don't show your net too long, because you will be asking students to make their own nets in just a minute.

Pass out cubes and white paper. You may want students to work with a partner. Tell them it is their job to make a net for the cube. Make sure they understand the two important conditions of the net. First, it can contain no extra paper, it must cover the cube exactly. Second, it must be continuous. They should not make several parts and put them on the figure. Tell students that usually when people make nets they make dotted lines to indicate where the net is to be folded. Also, ask students to take notes as they work telling how they approached the problem and what thinking or ideas they used as they made the net. Tell them to keep both successful and unsuccessful nets.

WHILE STUDENTS ARE ATTEMPTING TO MAKE NETS, walk around the room and observe them. Ask students questions about why they think their ideas will work. For example, point to a face on their net. Ask them to show you the corresponding face on the shape. Often students try the trial-and-error approach, when a little extra thinking would help. This use of communication may help them think first.

f.y.i.

This lesson takes the approach of having students try to make nets without studying other nets first or talking much about how to make them. Both of these will come later. This approach is taken to get the students to think visually rather than trying to remember and copy another person's idea.

What Might Happen . . . What to Do

Some students might be totally lost. Here are two ideas that might help them. First, have them try to cover the cube with the paper. They should cut out any paper that overlaps. They can crease the paper at the edges and possibly have a net. Another option is to make the six faces out of paper and tape them together one at a time. In using this method, students need to make sure they don't tape a face to two other faces. After they use these methods they should lay out their nets and study why they work.

After students have made their nets, get them back together to discuss what they did. There are two main goals for the discussion. First, you want to talk about what they considered and did to make their nets. This use of communication will help students benefit from each other's visual thinking and reasoning. Second, you want students to see that there are several different nets that work for cubes.

Net 1

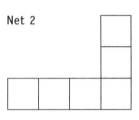

Works

Ask students to show their nets. Have them talk about their strategies for building the nets. Make sure they talk about their successes and also their failures. Help students realize they can learn as much, and sometimes more, from something that doesn't work as they can from something that works. Analyzing failures as well as successes will help them become better at reasoning.

Here are some possible strategies for making nets.

- Place the cube on the paper and trace the face. Roll the cube to another face. As you do this, mark the face you traced. Trace again. This is not a perfect method. Students have to make sure they can get to all the faces.
- Think visually about cutting the faces off the cube. This would be like peeling an onion. This is almost the reversal of the wrapping strategy.

Net 2

Does Not Work

As students are showing their nets, you can have them work on developing the ability to determine visually whether a net works or not. Have a student show his or her net. Have the other students tell whether they think this net will work to cover a cube. It is important to have students show some nets that don't work.

Net 3

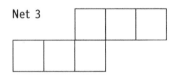

Works

If students are having trouble telling if a net will work, try this activity to help develop their visual perception. Have a person go up to the front of the room and show the class the net. Then make a copy of the net on the board. Ask students if they think the net will work or not. Then have the person with the net start attempting to wrap the cube with the net one face at a time. At the board, show the students which face on the net the demonstrator is working with. Your goal is to be a play-by-play announcer, telling what is happening while the net is being built, and showing students what is happening on the diagram. Include nets that don't work to help students see why they don't work.

To end the lesson, review with students what a net is. Have them do a brief review of the strategies they liked best for making and determining whether or not a net worked. Then tell them you would like them to do pages 86–87.

Extension

One possible extension continues the exercise with the cubes. There are 35 ways of putting 6 squares together. Some will fold into boxes; some will not. Interested students could try to find all 35 ways and determine which ones can be folded into cubes. (There are 15 possible nets for a cube.)

Student Pages

Student page 86 asks students to use their math reasoning to analyze several nets that are missing a face or two. Student page 87 gives the students three pairs of nets. Each pair has one net that will fold into a given shape and one that will not.

Assessment

You had an opportunity to assess students' understanding of nets while you observed them making their nets. As students talked about their strategies, you were able to go beyond whether they could complete the assignment, and get a sense of how they reasoned while attempting to accomplish a task. Finally, the student pages gave you an idea of what students could transfer to problems done on paper.

NCTM Standards Summary

Students developed their spatial thinking abilities and reasoning while trying to understand how two-dimensional nets can be made from three-dimensional objects. They identified and analyzed the attributes of these objects in both two and three dimensions. They analyzed shapes and reasoned about what kinds of nets could be constructed to make the objects. They also reasoned about which net was valid to make a given three-dimensional object. They communicated their thinking to help others gain insight into this concept.

Answers

Page 86
Answers may vary.

Page 87
1. A
2. The center of A can be wrapped around and the two sides folded right up. B cannot fold because there are 5 squares in a row.
3. B
4. In A, there are two faces that are opposite each other that are contiguous in the net.
5. B
6. In A, both of the circular portions of the cylinder are on the same side.

Investigating Nets

Complete the nets for the cubes. Start at the dotted line.

❶

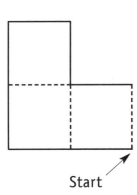

Start

❷

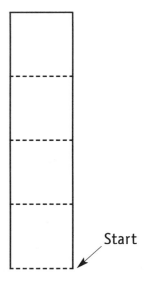

Start

❸

Start

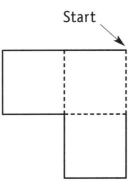

❹

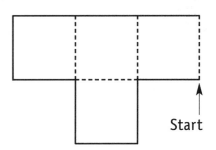

Start

Standard 3 Geometry

Investigating Nets

Carefully look at each net. Decide which one will fold and which one will not. Explain your thinking.

Cube   A.

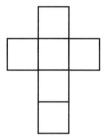

B.

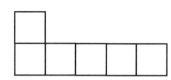

❶ Which one will fold into a cube?

❷ How do you know?

Rectangular
Prism   A.

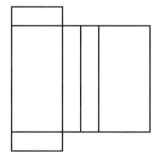

B.

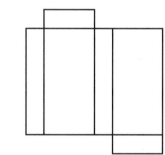

❸ Which one will fold into a rectangular prism?

❹ How do you know?

Cylinder   A.

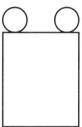

B.

❺ Which one will fold into a cylinder?

❻ How do you know?

Standard 3 Geometry

Exploring Circumference and Diameter

Introduction

Objective → Students will explore the relationship between the circumference and the diameter of a circle and develop an understanding of *pi*.

Context → Students have discussed parts of a circle, including the center point, radius, diameter, chord, and circumference. Students may have constructed circles using a compass. The lesson ends the unit on circles.

Exploring Circumference and Diameter

Learn

Materials: cm ruler; string; pencil; paper; several circular objects

The **circumference** is the perimeter of a circle. You already know how to find the perimeter around figures with straight sides, such as squares and triangles.

First, wrap the string around one of your round objects and mark where the string meets.

Second, lay the string out along the ruler to measure the length of the string.

Then, trace the circular object on a sheet of paper and measure the diameter.

Let's say you measured a can using a piece of string and found that the circumference was 62.8 cm. You then measured the diameter to be 20 cm.

Divide the circumference (*C*) by the diameter (*d*).

$62.8 \div 20 = 3.14$

Enter your measurements in the chart below.

Circle	Circumference (*C*)	Diameter (*d*)	*C* ÷ *d*
can	62.8 cm	20 cm	3.14 cm
object A			
object B			

NCTM Process Standards Analysis and Focus

The standards analysis examines how the process standards have been incorporated into the above lesson. By increasing the focus on three of the process standards, a more effective and meaningful lesson can be presented. The suggestions offered can help you to think about how this might be accomplished.

Problem Solving The lesson asks students to explore the relationship of the diameter of the circle to the circumference, but rather than allowing exploration, students are given information and told how to proceed. The problems at the end of the lesson appear to be problem solving, but, they don't relate to circumference.

Suggestion → Rather than telling students what relationship exists between

Try

Find the diameter and circumference of two more circular objects. Record your measurements in the table on the previous page. Divide the circumference of each object by its diameter. Round to the nearest hundredth.

You should have found that $C \div d$ was about 3.14.

The circumference of any circle divided by its diameter is 3.14, $C \div d$, and is known as *pi* (π).

How can you find the circumference of a circle without using the string method? Explain your answer.

Practice

Complete the table. Divide the circumference of each object by its diameter. Round to the nearest hundredth.

Object	Diameter (d)	Circumference (C)	$C \div d$
1. CD	11.8 cm	37.05 cm	?
2. bowl	17.6 cm	55.26 cm	?
3. spool	4.3 cm	13.50 cm	?
4. sm. pizza	12 in.	37.68 in.	?
5. lg. pizza	15 in.	46.80 in.	?
6. table	3 ft	9.42 ft	?

7. You have a cake with a 13-inch diameter. What is the perimeter of the smallest box the cake will fit in?

8. **Think About It** If you know the diameter of a circle, how could you find its circumference?

the diameter and circumference of a circle, have students gather and evaluate data to determine the relationship. An investigative approach that allows students to acquire information and synthesize results will produce learning that is more meaningful and will increase retention.

Reasoning and Proof The lesson sets the stage for gathering information but does not require students to compile and study information to reach a conclusion or explain their thinking.

Suggestion → Have students collect and analyze data, and encourage them to develop ideas and test them. Encourage them to reason about what constitutes a relationship between two quantities and determine if a relationship exists between the circumference and the diameter.

Communication Communication is limited.

Suggestion → Emphasize reasoning and proof in this lesson by prompting students to discuss their results and reasons with one another. Provide opportunities for students to listen to and evaluate the thinking of others.

Representation Students draw circles and record information in chart form. Variables are used in the lesson to represent *circumference, diameter,* and *pi.*

Connections The lesson makes a connection between perimeter and circumference.

The teaching plan that follows shows how the suggestions for increasing the focus on the process standards can be implemented.

Revised Teaching Plan

Materials → String; measuring tapes; rulers; compasses; calculators; an assortment of round items to measure, such as cans, thread spools, cups, and drinking glasses

BEGIN THE LESSON WITH A BRIEF REVIEW of circle vocabulary. Students will need to be comfortable with the terms *diameter, radius,* and *circumference* and their meanings to investigate the relationships between them effectively.

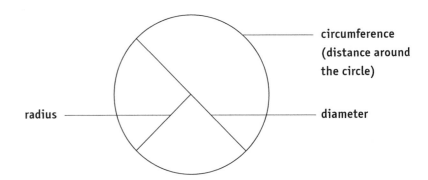

Invite students to consider how the parts of a circle are related. *Is there a relationship between the diameter of a circle and its circumference? If so, what is it?* Be prepared to clarify the term *relationship* by providing several examples and listing them in chart form on the board. Good examples include the length of a side of a square to its perimeter, the length of a side of a square to its area, the number of inches in a yard or a foot, and the number of tires on a car. Pose questions that encourage students to examine and extend their understanding of these relationships. *If there are 10 cars in a parking lot, how many tires are there? If a square's side doubles, by how much does its perimeter increase?* These questions make connections to knowledge of ratios, multiplication, and division and help students generalize from a list of specifics, a critical component of reasoning and proof.

O RGANIZE THE CLASS INTO GROUPS of three or four students. Ask each group to measure the circumference and diameter of several different-sized circular objects and look for a relationship between the two quantities.

As an alternative to having students gather their own measurements, use the data here. This will save time and still allow students to investigate the relationship between circumference and diameter. If you chose this option, give each group different data to work with.

$C = 45$ m	$d = 14.32$ m	$r = 26.82$ in.	$C = 168.5$ in.
$r = 12$ mi	$C = 75.4$ mi	$d = 93.26$ yd	$C = 293$ yd
$C = 110$ km	$r = 17.5$ km	$r = 1.91$ m	$C = 12$ m
$C = 570$ in.	$d = 181.44$ in.	$C = 50.3$ in.	$d = 16$ in.
$C = 62$ ft	$d = 19.74$ ft	$d = 114$ cm	$C = 358.14$ cm
$d = 112.68$ m	$C = 354$ m	$C = 226.20$ m	$r = 36$ m

Regardless of how the data are accumulated, allow students to choose their method of recording their findings. This will encourage students to engage their reasoning and will challenge and strengthen their ability to represent information.

What Might Happen . . . What to Do

Students might be unsure of how to proceed after measurements are gathered. Help students focus on organizing information and looking for patterns. *In what ways could we organize the measurements for diameter and circumference?*

Encourage students to determine how to express the difference between pairs of numbers and suggest that they approximate their answers. *About how much more is this circumference than this diameter? Is it about 5 inches more? Is it about twice as much? Are there any other ways we can express how much more it is? Is the relationship about the same for different pairs of numbers?*

To expedite progress, allow students to use calculators. This will prevent calculation errors from obscuring results. A brief review of reading and rounding decimals might be in order as students begin to organize their data.

As students work, circulate and ask questions to help group members communicate their thinking and their methods. *Describe the method you used to find these results. Why did you divide/multiply? Did you use the same method for all pairs? How do the results for different pairs of numbers compare?*

ALLOW TIME FOR STUDENTS to complete their investigations, and then gather the class for a final discussion. Create a table on the board into which each group can enter information in a consistent format. Organizing the data in this manner will make existing relationships more apparent.

Object	Radius	Diameter	Circumference	Relationship
CD	$2\frac{1}{2}$ in.	$4\frac{1}{2}$ in.	about 14 in.	Circumference is about 3 times the diameter.
Mug	4.5 cm	9 cm	about 28 cm	Diameter is about $\frac{1}{3}$ of the circumference.

Groups may present their findings in terms of either multiplication or division. This can provide a good opportunity to discuss the inverse relationship between the two operations and to reinforce the idea that there is more than one correct way to express a mathematical relationship.

Help students generalize the information. *What similarities exist in the results found by the different groups? How do the results vary? How does the size of the circle affect the information found? How can we describe the relationship between the circumference of a circle and its diameter? What about the relationship between the radius and the circumference?* Record responses on the board and translate words into symbolic form using ≈, the symbol for approximately equal. "Circumference is about 3 times the diameter" would be $C \approx 3d$, while "when the circumference is divided by the diameter, the result is about 3" would be $C/d \approx 3$.

Restate the conclusions reached and ask students to consider whether their findings about the relationship between circumference and diameter are conclusive. *Have we investigated enough circles to know that our conclusions are correct? How many circles would have to be checked? Five? Twenty? One hundred? Do you think there is any circle, of any size, for which the circumference is not about three times the diameter?* Although finding a proof of this relationship would not be possible, students should understand that further investigation would be appropriate and that discovering a counter example would disprove their thinking.

CONCLUDE THE LESSON by asking students to estimate the circumference of a circle when given the diameter or radius and to estimate the diameter or radius when given the circumference.

Estimate the circumference from the radius or diameter given.

$d = 7$ in. (21 in.) $r = 5$ ft (30 ft) $d = 2$ cm (6 cm) $r = 2$ yd (12 yd)

Estimate the diameter of a circle with the given circumference.

300 in. (100 in.)   27 ft (9 ft)   486 cm (162 cm)

Estimate the radius of a circle with the given circumference.

36 yd (6 yd)   261 m (43.5 m)

Student Pages

Students should now be ready to complete exercises similar to those on the reduced student pages.

Assessment

Assessment opportunities occurred throughout the lesson as students participated in group work and in class discussions. As they analyzed data and made generalizations, you could determine students' level of understanding and their ability to reason about the relationship between a circle's circumference and its diameter.

NCTM Standards Summary

Making problem solving the focus of this lesson involved students in their own learning. Having students examine sets of data to determine whether a relationship exists between parts of a circle, and what that relationship is, set the stage for increased reasoning and proof and communication. Students thought about and discussed the information they found, drew conclusions, explained thinking, and employed critical thinking as they evaluated their findings. Students also learned the importance of representing data in appropriate ways through the use of charts and simple formulas that symbolize the relationships they explored.

Standard 4 **Measurement**

AT THE FIFTH GRADE LEVEL, measurement includes work with finding the total surface area and the volume of rectangular solids, and a lot of work with measuring length. Our lessons are derived from these important topics. They include a lesson on finding the volume of a rectangular solid, a lesson on finding the total surface area of a rectangular solid, a lesson that introduces precision of measurement, and a lesson on converting measurements between customary units of length.

Three lessons model how the process standards can be used to teach content. A fourth lesson is a hypothetical textbook lesson that we have revised to be more standards based. These four lessons do not represent the entire curriculum, but rather provide glimpses of how, with a more concentrated effort to incorporate the process standards, better mathematics teaching and learning can be achieved.

One lesson we have chosen leads students to the formula for finding the volume of a rectangular solid. This lesson is driven by the process standards of problem solving, representation, and reasoning and proof. Students are presented with rectangular solids or prisms, and use cubes to fill or replicate them to find the volume. Students deduce the formula for volume from their results.

Another lesson we have chosen has students calculate the surface area of a rectangular solid. Instead of just being presented with a formula, students are presented with a problem-solving situation in which they have to use the least amount of paper possible to cover a rectangular solid. They connect their knowledge of finding the area of a rectangle to finding the total surface area of the solid.

A third lesson we have chosen introduces students to the notion that measurement is approximate, and to the concept of precision in measurement. Using the process standards of representation, communication, and connections, students will better understand the range of measurements that a particular measurement represents, and why using a smaller unit leads to a more precise measurement.

The hypothetical textbook lesson we have chosen to revise is one in which students are to convert measurements of length between the customary units of inches, feet, yards, and miles. Through greater incorporation of the process standards of representation, communication, and connections, students will better understand the relationships between the units as well as develop a better sense of what operations are needed to perform the conversions.

Standard 4 Lessons

**Finding Volume of
Rectangular Solids**

Exploring Surface Area

Investigating Measurement

**Converting Among Standard
Units of Length**

Finding Volume of Rectangular Solids

Introduction

- -

Objective → Students will determine a formula for finding the volume.

Context → Students have previously worked with cubes to first estimate and then find the volume of rectangular prisms. After connecting these experiences with finding volume by using the standard formula $V = lwh,$ they will go on to explore the volume of other solids.

NCTM Standards Focus

Often students are introduced to the formula for finding the volume of rectangular prisms and are expected to apply it to a series of figures. By building models of rectangular solids with cubes, students see a concrete representation of volume. These hands-on experiences lay the foundation for understanding and applying the standard formula for finding the volume of rectangular prisms. In this standards-based lesson, students connect concrete experiences with the more abstract representation for finding volume—a formula.

Problem Solving Students determine the number of cubes needed to build a model of a rectangular solid. They problem solve to find a more efficient method for calculating the volume without building a complete model or filling an entire container.

Representation Students build models of rectangular prisms with cubes. These cubes represent cubic units—the appropriate measure for finding volume. This visual representation of volume helps solidify student understanding and also provides a mental reference when working with the formula.

Reasoning and Proof Students look for a more efficient method for finding the volume of rectangular prisms. They may take different routes such as looking for similarities to other formulas they might know or looking at the concept of stacking layers to help them make a generalization of how to find the volume.

Teaching Plan

Materials → Student pages 100–101; some type of stackable cube (centimeter or inch cubes will work best when translating to actual measures)

BEGIN THE LESSON BY SHOWING students a rectangular prism that has been built with cubes. Ask them to describe the prism. *What are the attributes of this rectangular prism? What are some other examples of rectangular prisms?* Next review with them the concept of volume. Make sure you mention that we record volume in terms of cubic measurements. Referring to the rectangular prism that is built with cubes will help.

What Might Happen . . . What to Do

Some students may confuse volume with capacity. Although volume and capacity are similar concepts it is important to note the difference between the two. Volume is a measure of the space an object takes up, while capacity is a measure of the amount of liquid that a container can hold. It may take a while for students to make this distinction. Reviewing the different measures for volume and capacity in everyday situations can help.

f.y.i.

Encourage students to see that since they knew the number of cubes for the first problem, they could simply calculate the number of cubes that would be needed to make two more layers.

Have students work in groups. Give each student a copy of page 100. Tell them that today they will be trying to find a method for determining how many cubes it will take to build a rectangular prism without actually building it. The first task is to discover a method for accurately predicting how many cubes would be needed to build each prism. The purpose of the activity is to have students determine a method for finding volume informally. This will give them a conceptual foundation for understanding and using volume formulas. Encourage students to use their cubes, but caution them not to build the entire prism before first predicting how many cubes will be needed to build it. Have students record their methods so they can share them with the class. Once students have recorded their predictions and methods, have them verify their predictions by building the prisms. If the number of cubes needed did not match a student's prediction, have the student analyze the method used to make the prediction and try to revise the method.

CONTINUE THE LESSON by engaging the class in a discussion about what methods they used to make their predictions. *Did your method give you the correct number of cubes needed? Why do you think your method worked? Did you use the same method for both problems? Do you think your method would work for all rectangular prisms?* If no one volunteers a method that did not work, suggest one or two and ask students to explain why the methods don't work.

One method that students may have used is to calculate the number of cubes needed for one layer of the prism by using what they know about area. Then they can look at the height to find out how many layers there are and multiply to find the total number of cubes. Some students may have used the cubes to construct the bottom layer of the prism, counted the cubes, and then multiplied by the number of layers. Others may have used the cubes to construct a different face and then multiplied by the number of layers of that face.

AS THE DISCUSSION PROCEEDS, it is likely students will mention some method that resembles multiplying length by width by height. If not, be sure to propose the method and have students verify that it works.

Write on the board the methods students think are worthwhile to use to find the volume. Discuss with them whether they think a method will work in all cases and why. Have them suggest several different rectangular prisms to try with their methods to see if they can find a case where the method doesn't work. By challenging the students to find a counterexample, you are focusing on reasoning and proof.

After students agree that some of the methods will work in all cases, have the students write them in as short a form as possible. Ask students to share their methods. Again, some form of the standard formula for the volume should surface. If not, suggest it. Have students analyze the formula and relate it to the problems on page 100. Continue the discussion until students are convinced that the formula makes sense.

What Might Happen . . . What to Do

Some students may have difficulty expressing their ideas as a formula or set of steps. Build all the layers out on the table. Ask students how many are in one layer and how many layers there are. As they determine the total, stack the layers to make the prism. Model this procedure on the board so students can see it as a method that can translate into length times width times height.

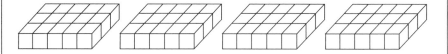

Tell students you would like to see if they can apply their methods or formulas to three-dimensional drawings of rectangular prisms. Draw a simple rectangular prism and label it with a width of 4 cm, a length of 2 cm, and a height of 7 cm. Ask students to use the formula $V = lwh$. Review with them that the answer should be expressed in cubic centimeters. Relate this to the fact that their earlier answers were in cubes. If you were able to use centimeter cubes this should be clear. If need be, do a few more examples and have them relate the formula back to the activity at the beginning of the lesson. Have the students complete the exercises on page 101.

Student Pages

Student page 100 provides an illustration of the two cubes and space for student responses for the class activity. Student page 101 gives students practice applying their method or the formula $V = lwh$.

Assessment

While students represented the volume of rectangular prisms or solids using cubes, you observed them make connections between volume and length, width, and height. You assessed students' reasoning skills as they determined a method for finding the volume of rectangular solids. As students did page 101 you assessed their ability to transfer what they had represented concretely to a more abstract, but more efficient, method for finding volume.

NCTM Standards Summary

Students used cubes and rectangular prisms to explore the concept of volume. They used problem-solving skills to look for the most efficient means of finding the volume of several objects. By using a physical representation of volume measures (cubes), they could see how knowing the length, width, and height of a rectangular prism allowed them to find the volume. They reasoned a method for finding this volume efficiently.

Answers

Page 100
1. Predictions and methods may vary. 60 cubes
2. Predictions and methods may vary. 90 cubes

Page 101
1. 96 cubic units
2. 210 cubic units
3. 480 cubic units
4. 567 cubic units
5. 270 cubic units
6. 245 cubic units

Finding Volume of Rectangular Solids

❶ Predict how many cubes you will need to build the prism.
Describe how you made your prediction. Build the prism to test your prediction.

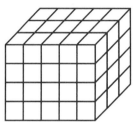

Prediction _____   Actual Number of Cubes _____

How I made my prediction:

_____

_____

_____

❷ Predict how many cubes you will need to build the prism.
Describe how you made your prediction. Build the prism to test your prediction.

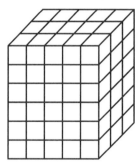

Prediction _____   Actual Number of Cubes _____

How I made my prediction:

_____

_____

_____

Standard 4 Measurement

Finding Volume of Rectangular Solids

Find the volume.

1

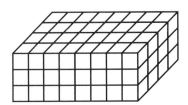

Volume = _____

2

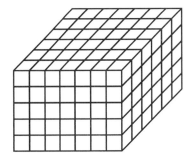

Volume = _____

3

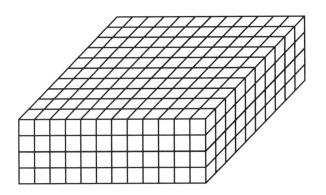

Volume = _____

4

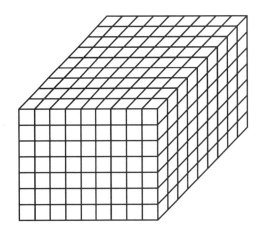

Volume = _____

5

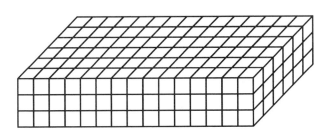

Volume = _____

6

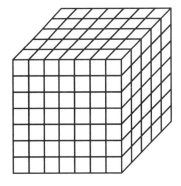

Volume = _____

Standard 4 Measurement

Exploring Surface Area

Introduction

Objective → Students will be able to calculate the surface area of a rectangular solid.

Context → Students are familiar with finding the area of rectangles. They are ready to apply this understanding to an exploration of the surface area of rectangular solids. They will go on to learn and apply the formula for finding surface area.

f.y.i.

You may want the solids you use for this lesson to have sides that are a whole number of units long. You may want to construct your own solids to be sure that sides do not have fraction or decimal measures.

NCTM Standards Focus

In this lesson, students apply their knowledge of area by exploring the surface area of rectangular solids. They are presented with problem-solving situations in which they engage in a hands-on exploration of this concept. Traditionally, students are given abstract measures and asked to calculate surface area without understanding what they are doing or how it applies to the real world. In this standards-based lesson, students physically manipulate materials to explore surface area and connect these experiences to meaningful contexts.

Problem Solving Students use their problem-solving skills to determine how much contact paper they would need to cover a storage box (a rectangular solid). They use a problem-solving approach to determine the smallest amount of contact paper they would need to cover a given solid and how best to use it.

Connections Students connect their understanding of area to finding the surface area of rectangular solids. They also make connections between their hands-on classroom experiences and "real world" situations.

Teaching Plan

Materials → Student pages 106–107; centimeter rulers; centimeter grid paper; 1 small rectangular prism for each pair of students; a cereal or similar box that can easily be cut apart and laid flat; large construction paper or butcher paper; scissors; tape or glue

ASK STUDENTS TO IMAGINE the following scenario: *These objects are storage containers that you want to cover with colorful contact paper. You have a limited supply of contact paper and you want to figure out the minimum amount of paper needed to completely cover each shape.* Hold up a solid for students to see. Ask them how they could find out how much contact paper would be needed to cover the solid.

Allow students to grapple with the problem. After giving them time to think through the problem, have them share some of their strategies with the class. Listen carefully as students break the problem down into smaller chunks. If these questions (and corresponding answers) don't surface in the student discussion, present them to the class.

- *How many sides or faces do you need to cover?* (6)
- *Are all of the sides congruent or the same shape and size?* (Only when working with a cube.)
- *How could you find the amount of paper needed to cover one face or side?* (Measure and find the area of the face.)
- *How do you find the area of a rectangle?* (Multiply the length times the width.)
- *What units are used for measuring area?* (Square units)

Introduce students to the term "surface area." Explain that when they found the total area of the solid to be covered with contact paper, they found the solid's surface area. *Can the same method be used to find the surface area of any rectangular solid? What rule or formula can we state for finding the surface area of any rectangular prism?* (To find the surface area of a rectangular prism, find the sum of the areas of all of the faces of the prism.)

Point out that another way to think about surface area of a rectangular prism is to imagine the prism cut apart at the edges and laid flat. Demonstrate this to the class using a cereal, or similar, box.

PAIR STUDENTS OFF AND HAND OUT student page 106 to each student. Give centimeter rulers, scissors, and some butcher or construction paper to each pair. Tell them to select one solid to explore. You might suggest that students label the faces of the solids with the letters A–F to help them organize their measurements. Once they've completed their measurements and calculated the surface area of that solid, they should trade shapes with another pair. Each pair should measure and find the surface area of two shapes. Once they've completed their measurements, have students

f.y.i.

You might want to work through an entire example with students. If so, make a chart similar to the one on student page 106. Working through this example with the whole group will give students a model to refer to when working on their own.

f.y.i.

Be sure that student pairs first do the problem using a rectangular solid that has at least one pair of faces that are squares. Later they may want to try the problem with prisms that do not have any square faces. If some students are really stuck, you might suggest that they start with a cube, perhaps even a $1 \times 1 \times 1$ cube, followed by a $1 \times 1 \times 2$ prism.

share their results. *Has anyone discovered that each prism has three pairs of congruent faces?* If not, guide students to recognize this fact by using one of the shapes as a model. *How does knowing that opposite faces of a rectangular prism are congruent make it easier to find the surface area?* (You can measure one face from each pair, multiply by 2, and add the three resulting products together.)

CONCLUDE THE LESSON by presenting students with a model of a rectangular prism they have not worked with (e.g., a shoebox). Give them the measurements for the length, width, and height of the box. Have students find the surface area for the object and share their results and strategies.

Hand out student page 107. Instruct students to attempt these problems on their own, but to ask for help from others if they get stuck. Tell them that they may want to refer to the charts they completed on student page 106 to use as tools for finding the surface area of the four figures given.

Extension

Assign the problem at the bottom of page 106 to pairs of students. The problem is an interesting and complex one that will test the visualization skill of many students. Having students work in pairs may encourage them to experiment with different solution strategies.

While students work with their partners, observe the variety of problem-solving strategies they use. Watch to see the different approaches students use to solve the problem.

Methods Students Might Use

- Cut out as many rectangles as possible with the appropriate area. Begin cutting and covering the faces of their shapes until they find a rectangle that works.

- Before cutting out the rectangle with the appropriate area, measure and lightly mark rectangles for the different faces, seeing how certain cuts would affect the whole project. Make adjustments as they see necessary.

- Draw the different faces on paper (to proper scale) and try to see how they could be placed together to create the best single rectangle. Once the most efficient rectangle has been identified, then cut out the large rectangle and make cuts according to their plans.

- Construct rectangles for each face. Place these rectangles together to form a shape as close to a perfect rectangle as possible. Cut out a single rectangle using these measurements, then replicate their original pieces.

Student Pages

Student page 106 provides two charts for students to record the measurements and area of each face of a rectangular solid, as well as the total surface area. In addition, students are given a problem-solving situation. Student page 107 shows four rectangular prisms. Students are to find the surface area of each figure.

Assessment

You had the opportunity to observe students as they explored the concept of surface area. You saw students make the connection between the area of each face and the total surface area of the object. You observed them discover that each rectangular prism has three pairs of congruent faces or sides. You could then assess whether or not students transferred this information to problem-solving situations.

NCTM Standards Summary

In exploring the concept of surface area, students made connections to previous learning about area and how it applies to finding the surface area of rectangular prisms. They then engaged in a problem-solving experience when they applied their understanding of surface area to a real-world situation. Finally, given only the dimensions of figures, they calculated the surface area of each figure, connecting their previous concrete representational experiences to a more abstract problem-solving technique.

Answers

Page 106
Student measurements and responses will vary.

Page 107
1. 184 square cm (184 cm^2)
2. 266 square inches (266 in.^{2})
3. 222 square feet (222 ft^2)
4. 318 square meters (318 m^2)
5. Answers will vary.

Exploring Surface Area

Record the measurements for each face of the rectangular solids you use. Find the area of each face, then the total surface area of the object.

❶

Face	Length	Width	Area
A			
B			
C			
D			
E			
F			

Surface Area	

❷

Face	Length	Width	Area
A			
B			
C			
D			
E			
F			

Surface Area	

❸ Think of a rectangular prism that has at least one pair of faces that are squares. What is the surface area of the prism? Draw the all rectangles that have an area equal to the total surface area of the prism. Is there a way to cut any of the rectangles into smaller rectangles so that they cover the faces of the solid exactly?

Standard 4 Measurement

Exploring Surface Area

Find the surface area for each figure shown.
Be sure to record all area measures in square units.

❶

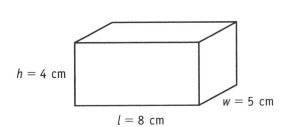

$h = 4$ cm
$w = 5$ cm
$l = 8$ cm

Surface area = _____

❷

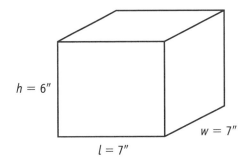

$h = 6''$
$w = 7''$
$l = 7''$

Surface area = _____

❸

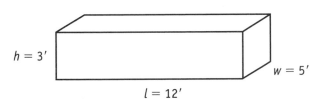

$h = 3'$
$w = 5'$
$l = 12'$

Surface area = _____

❹

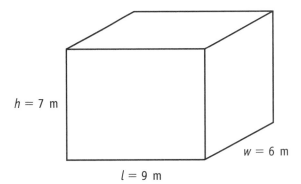

$h = 7$ m
$w = 6$ m
$l = 9$ m

Surface area = _____

❺ Explain how you found the surface area of these figures.

_____

_____

_____

_____

_____

Standard 4 Measurement

Investigating Measurement

Introduction

Objective → Students will understand why all measurements are approximate and compare the precision of measurements.

Context → This lesson comes at the end of a study of measurement in which students have learned about customary and metric units. They have worked with decimals and understand decimal place value. Students will go on to apply measurement concepts as they solve problems involving perimeter, area, and volume.

NCTM Standards Focus

In this standards-based lesson, students will explore how approximation is involved in the measurement process. They will learn that the precision of a measurement is affected by the measuring tool used.

Representation Students will conduct a series of linear measurements and represent lengths of objects in metric units. As they compare measurements, students will examine how the precision of the measurement is impacted by the instrument used.

Communication Students will communicate measurements and observations about the measuring process both orally and in writing. They will discuss precision and will suggest measurement situations that require varying degrees of precision.

Connections Students will utilize prior knowledge of the metric system and decimal place value as they consider how the unit of a measurement must be examined to determine the precision of the measurement. Connections to real-life situations will be made as students think about the need for precise measurements.

Teaching Plan

Materials → Student pages 112–113; an assortment of measuring tools including meter sticks and/or metric measuring tapes; cm/mm rulers

B EGIN THE LESSON by having students describe situations in which they have taken measurements. Have them tell why the measurement was needed, what kind of measuring tool and unit they used, and how the measurement was recorded. *Do you think that your measurements were exact? Why?* (No. They may not have measured accurately; measurements may have been rounded.) Explain that all measurements are approximate and tell students that in this lesson they will explore this concept.

Arrange students in pairs and provide each pair with a copy of student page 112. Explain that they are to complete the first investigation on the worksheet by identifying two items in the classroom to fit each of the four descriptions. Have students interpret the meaning of the *greater than* (>) and *less than* (<) symbols as used on the page. Make sure they understand that in two of the cases they must find items that fall between two different measurements.

Tell students to record the names of the items and their lengths. Circulate as students work and observe their use of the measurement tools.

What Might Happen . . . What to Do

Students may have difficulty identifying items whose lengths fall within a given range, such as between 100 cm and 150 cm. Guide them in determining appropriate lengths by asking questions. *Show me with your hands about how big* *a meter length would be. Are you looking for something longer or shorter? Would 150 cm be more or less than a meter? How do you know? Based on your estimate of a meter, about how big would 150 cm be?*

Have students discuss their findings and record the items suggested for each category in a class chart on the board. *How do you know that object fits here?* Insist that students convince you that their objects are, indeed, correctly placed.

ASK STUDENTS TO ORDER the items measuring between 100 cm and 150 cm from shortest to longest and discuss their results. Different positions may have been assigned to objects, especially if some objects are relatively close in length. *How can the order of these items be resolved?* If students don't suggest measuring the objects again and making more careful or closer readings, offer the idea. Discuss that measuring "more carefully" includes using the tool properly and using a tool that allows measuring in smaller units. Students may intuitively recognize that using a smaller unit helps to make a closer approximation of the actual measure.

Instruct students to work with their partners to complete student page 112. Students will need a cm/mm ruler. Discuss their answers to the third question; some students may have found the length to be 127 mm while others may have rounded down to 126 mm based on their visual interpretation. The difference is not a key issue here. *Is either of these two measurements exact? Why or why not?* (No. The length of the ribbon was between two marks for the unit being used.) *Which do you think is a better approximation of the exact length? Explain.* (126 mm. The length is less than 127.5 mm.)

f.y.i.

A general statement about the range of lengths that would be reported as 98 dm would be 97.5 ≤ length < 98.5. The actual measurement lies between the measurement ± half the precision of the measurement.

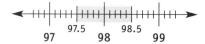

CONTINUE THE DISCUSSION on precision by explaining that a measurement of 127 mm is said to be *more precise* than a measurement of 13 cm; the smaller the unit used to measure, the more precise the measure. Clarify this concept by posing questions to help students compare the precision of 98 dm with that of 980 cm. Illustrate the concept with a drawing on the board or overhead.

- *What measurements would round to 98 decimeters?* (97.5 dm through any measurement less than 98.5 dm)
- *What unit of measure does the 5 in 97.5 dm represent?* (cm)
- *What does this tell us about a measurement recorded as 98 decimeters?* (It can be as much as 5 cm less or almost 5 cm more than 98 dm; there is a range of about 10 dm.)
- *How many centimeters are included in the range for measuring to the nearest decimeter?* (10 cm)
- *What amounts would round to 980 centimeters?* (979.5 cm through any measurement less than 980.5 cm)
- *What unit of measure does the 5 in 979.5 cm represent?* (mm)
- *What does this tell us about a measurement recorded as 980 centimeters?* (It can be as much as 5 mm less or almost 5 mm more than 980 cm; there is a range of about 10 mm.)
- *Which measurement, 98 decimeters or 980 centimeters, would be more precise? Why?* (980 cm; 980 cm is precise to the nearest cm within a range of 10 mm. This is much smaller than the range of 10 cm for 98 dm, which is precise to the nearest dm.)

You might consider working through another example by asking students to compare 4 m and 4.0 m. *Which would be a more precise measurement, 4 m or 4.0 m? Why?* (4.0 m is more precise since it is based on a range of about 10 cm, which is a smaller amount than the range of 10 dm on which 4 m is based.) Emphasize that these examples highlight how both the number and unit must be examined to determine the precision of a measurement.

Next, instruct pairs to draw a line segment exactly 3 centimeters long, and under it, create four different line segments, all of which, when reported to the nearest centimeter, would be 3 centimeters. Have students report lengths they drew. *What is the shortest line that can be called 3 cm?* (2.5 cm or 2 cm and 5 mm) *What is the longest?* (Just under 3.5 cm or 3 cm and 5 mm) Repeat the activity using 3 decimeters as the gauge. Have students compare the lengths of the extremes for both cases to see that those for the smaller unit are much closer to the actual length. This visual representation reinforces how using smaller units results in greater precision with a closer approximation to the actual measure.

Conclude the lesson by engaging students in a discussion of real-life situations where measurement precision is important versus those where approximation is acceptable. For example, a computer chip needs to be measured more precisely than a rug. The substances in a prescription medicine needed to be measured more precisely than the juices in a punch. Encourage students to communicate their ideas, either verbally or in writing, about one situation of each type in their daily lives.

Student Pages

Student page 112 provides space for students to record objects and their lengths for the first activity and a ribbon to be measured for the second activity. Page 113 gives students the opportunity to apply their understanding of precision of measurement.

Assessment

It was possible to assess the methods students used to determine measurements as they identified and measured classroom items. As students shared their thoughts about measurement situations and discussed precision of measurement, it was possible to evaluate their thinking about the appropriateness of precise or approximate measurements and to judge their understanding of this concept.

NCTM Standards Summary

In an investigation approach to understanding precision in measurement, students identified items that represented given lengths, recorded, and then compared their findings. By discussing what amounts a measurement represents and drawing lines to represent a measurement, students clarified their understanding of precision and the measurement process. As they took and interpreted measurements, students made connections to their knowledge of metric units and decimal place value. Making connections to real-life situations helped students to recognize that both the purpose of the measurement and the measuring tool used influence the precision of the measurement.

Answers

Page 112
1. Answers may vary.
2. 12 cm; 13 cm
   13 cm; 12 cm
   13 cm
3. 126 mm; 127 mm
   126 mm; 127 cm
   126 mm

Page 113
1. in. or $\frac{1}{4}$ in.
2. 0.1L or deciliter
3. cm or $\frac{1}{2}$ cm
4. 0.2 lb or pound (or another unit of weight)
5. 201 mm
6. 5.0 cm
7. 71 cm
8. 37 in.
9. They have the same precision.
10. 53.2 mm
11. Sara. Her measurement is precise to the nearest tenth of a cm while Roberto's is precise only to the nearest cm.
12. Answers may vary.

Investigating Measurement

1 Identify two items to represent each measurement. Write the name of the item.
Then measure each item and record its length. Be sure to include the unit of measurement used.

< 1 m   > 1 m

_____   _____

_____   _____

> 100 cm and < 150 cm   > 150 cm and < 200 cm

_____   _____

_____   _____

2 Measure the ribbon using centimeters and complete each sentence.

The ribbon is between _____ cm and _____ cm long.

The length is nearer to _____ cm than to _____ cm.

The length of the ribbon is _____ cm to the nearest centimeter.

3 Measure the same ribbon using millimeters and complete each sentence.

The ribbon is between _____ mm and _____ mm long.

The length is nearer to _____ mm than to _____ mm.

The length of the ribbon is _____ mm to the nearest millimeter.

Standard 4 Measurement

Investigating Measurement

For questions 1–4, name the unit of precision.

❶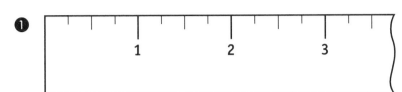

❷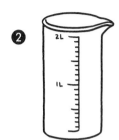

❸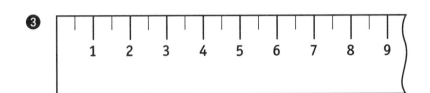

❹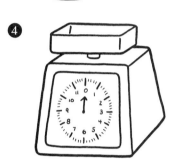

Circle the measurement in each pair that is more precise.

❺ 21 cm or 201 mm

❻ 5 cm or 5.0 cm

❼ 78 m or 71 cm

❽ 37 in. or 371 ft

❾ 264 cm or 2.64 m

❿ 53.2 mm or 5.3 cm

⓫ Roberto and Sara measured a bracelet. Roberto wrote his measurement as 14 cm. Sara wrote her measurement as 14.0 cm. Roberto said there was no difference in the two measurements because they both used centimeters. Sara said her measurement was more precise. Who is correct? Explain your answer.

⓬ Make up a set of three measurements. Ask a classmate to write the measurements in order from most precise to least precise. Then check your classmate's answer.

Converting Among Standard Units of Length

Introduction

Objective → Students will convert measurements of length among inches, feet, yards, and miles.

Context → This lesson ends a unit in which students have added and subtracted fractions with and without common denominators.

Converting Among Standard Units of Length

Learn

You can change among units of feet, yards, and miles.

Shaquille's bedroom is 4 yd 2 ft wide. Paul's bedroom is 14 feet wide. Whose bedroom is wider?

Change 4 yards to feet. Multiply to change greater units to lesser units.

1 yd = 3 ft

4 yd = 12 ft

4 yd 2 ft = 12 ft + 2 ft = 14 ft

Shaquille's and Paul's bedrooms are the same width.

Marcy entered her frog in a frog-jumping contest. The frog jumped two times.

First Jump   63 in.

Second Jump   5 ft 8 in.

Which jump was longer? You can change units to compare.

Change 63 inches to feet. Divide to change lesser units to greater units.

1 ft = 12 in.

$$12\overline{)63}$$
$$\underline{60}$$
$$5$$

3 extra inches

The second jump, 5 ft 8 in., is the longer jump.

Explain how you changed from one unit to another in the previous problems.

Try

1. 5 yd = _____ ft

2. 2 mi = _____ yd

3. 17 in. = _____ ft _____ in.

4. 5 mi 200 yd = _____ yd

5. Have you ever heard the phrase "Give an inch and they will take a mile"? How many inches are there in a mile?

NCTM Process Standards Analysis and Focus

The standards analysis examines how the process standards have been incorporated into the above lesson. By increasing the focus on three of the process standards, a more effective and meaningful lesson can be presented. The suggestions offered can help you to think about how this might be accomplished.

Representation An example on the student pages demonstrates a procedure for dividing to change smaller units to larger ones and multiplying to change larger units to smaller ones.

Suggestion → Increase attention to the exchange rates and relationships between units of measure. Have students measure the same items in different units. This will provide concrete representations of the relationships between

Learn

6. 12 yd = ■ ft   **7.** 144 in. = ■ ft   **8.** 2 mi = ■ ft

9. 4 mi = ■ yd   **10.** 5 ft 4 in. = ■ in.   **11.** 21,120 ft = ■ mi

12. 34 in. = ■ ft ■ in.   **13.** 15,840 ft = ■ mi   **14.** 5 yd 2 ft = ■ ft

Seeing patterns

15. Complete the chart showing the patterns of inches and feet.

Number of inches	12	24	36	__	60
Number of feet	1	__	__	4	__

To change inches to feet, _____ the number of inches by 12.
To change feet to inches, multiply the number of feet by _____.

16. Complete the chart showing the patterns of feet and yards.

Number of feet	3	6	__	12	__
Number of yards	1	__	3	__	5

To change feet to yards, divide the number of feet by _____.
To change yards to feet, _____ the number of yards by 3.

Problem Solving

17. Ansel drove for three hours at 55 mph and Tina drove two and a half hours at 60 mph. What is the difference in the total number of miles each drove? Give your answer in yards and feet.

18. The World Trade Center in New York City is 1350 feet tall. The Sears Tower in Chicago is 1454 feet tall. How much taller is the Sears Tower? Give your answer in yards and inches.

19. A football field is 100 yards in length. How many inches is that?

units and help students understand the use of division and multiplication to convert.

Communication Students are encouraged to explain how they decide whether to multiply or divide to change from one unit to another.

Suggestion → Provide ample opportunity to discuss how units are related, different ways to name equivalent measures, and the rationale for renaming.

This will help students develop a feel for the renaming process rather than depending on rote, mechanical approaches to renaming units.

Connections The lesson connects changing units to multiplication and division.

Suggestion → Help students make connections between all mathematical operations and unit conversions. Demonstrate how smaller units can be

represented as fractions of larger units. Also point out that conversions from smaller units to larger units often requires a combination of operations, such as repeated subtraction or a combination of division and subtraction.

Reasoning and Proof A discussion question asks students to explain the procedures used as they changed from unit to another.

Problem Solving Activities labeled problem solving are actually computation exercises that involve changing units. Because the lesson provides a procedure to solve these exercises, no problem solving is required.

The teaching plan that follows shows how the suggestions for increasing the focus on the process standards can implemented.

Revised Teaching Plan

Materials → Rulers; measuring tapes; yardsticks; calculators; a variety of objects of different lengths

Preparation → Prior to class, set up several measurement stations. Include items with whole unit lengths (objects that are an exact number of feet) and items that require mixed units (a bookcase that is 4 ft 8 in. high).

START THE LESSON by introducing the concept of inches, feet, and yards as units of linear measure. Initiate a discussion in which students can select which of these units they might use to measure various lengths. This will focus students' thinking on the relative sizes of units and which units would be more appropriate for measuring the given lengths. *Would you measure the width of your desk in inches, feet, or yards? Why? What about your height? The length of a pencil? The height of the door? The length of the room? The hallway?* As students give their answers, ask them to explain their choice of units.

Organize ideas about unit selection with two overlapping topics: convention and convenience. An example of convention is using yards to measure distances in football. *Would anyone know what you were talking about if you said a football player rushed for 900 feet in the game? What if you said 10,800 inches? Those are the same distances as 300 yards, so why wouldn't you use feet or inches?* An example of convenience is measuring a long distance in miles. *It's 11 miles from here to the next town. That's the same thing as 696,960 inches. Why do we usually measure distances between cities in miles instead of inches?* Broach the topic of accuracy. *Is it necessary to know how far it is to the next town down to the nearest inch?*

After students have talked about the unit of measure they have chosen, have them discuss why it is sometimes necessary to change from one unit to another. *Suppose you measured a baby in inches and wanted to find out how much shorter a baby is than an adult. Adults are usually measured in feet and inches. How can we compare these different kinds of measurement?* This discussion sets up the rationale for the lesson.

f.y.i.

- -

Generally, it is easier to measure longer lengths with larger units and to use smaller units for shorter lengths. Also, after a frame of reference for the units has been established, it is often easier to envision larger units such as 5 yards rather than 180 inches.

What Might Happen . . . What to Do

Students may disagree on which would be a more appropriate unit to use to measure some items. Allow them to explain their thinking, and help them understand that there is no right or wrong answer when selecting units. Remind students that unit choices usually involve a combination of convention and convenience, and point out that there can even be a conflict between those two factors. For example, comparing heights might be easier if all heights are expressed in inches, but people are usually measured in feet. *Is it easier to find the difference between 5 feet 2 inches and 4 feet 10 inches or the difference between 62 inches and 58 inches?*

REVIEW BASIC EQUIVALENT MEASURES for the standard units of length. Write the information on the board, and ask students to create conversion charts on paper for their own use.

$$
\begin{aligned}
12 \text{ in.} &= 1 \text{ ft} \\
3 \text{ ft} &= 1 \text{ yd} \\
36 \text{ in.} &= 1 \text{ yd} \\
1{,}760 \text{ yd} &= 1 \text{ mi} \\
5{,}280 \text{ ft} &= 1 \text{ mi}
\end{aligned}
$$

Help students develop a feel for these exchange rates by focusing their thinking on the proportional relationships between units. *How many times bigger than a foot is a yard? What fraction of a yard is a foot? What fraction of a foot is 6 inches? How many inches would there be in a foot and a half? How many feet are equal to $\frac{2}{3}$ yard? How many inches would that be?*

Have rulers, yardsticks, and measuring tapes available, and pair or group students to identify each of the three units: an inch, a foot, and a yard. Have them identify references for these measurements. They can identify parts of their body or familiar objects that are about the length of each unit. For example, from the tip of a finger to the first knuckle might be about an inch, and the length of an arm from elbow to fist might be close to a foot, and so on.

f.y.i.

Feet and yards have an interesting history. In ancient times the foot was so called because that was a part of the body that was a close approximation to that unit of measurement. At first, feet and yards were different lengths in different places. It is said that in 1320, King Edward II of England issued a decree that the standardized foot should equal the length of a row of 36 barleycorns, believed to have been the actual length of his own foot. Some accounts also suggest that the yard was defined as the king's girth. Today, the unit of one foot corresponds to an adult man's shoe size in Britain of $13\frac{1}{2}$–14, and in the United States of 14–$14\frac{1}{2}$.

ASSIGN STUDENTS TO WORK IN PAIRS or small groups to measure the various objects placed at measurement stations. Tell students to measure items in whole inches, feet, and yards as well as in combinations of inches and feet, feet and yards, and a mixture of all three units. For some of the items, leave the unit choice up to students; for some items, specify the units to use to ensure that students have experience with different combinations of mixed units. Instruct students to measure a few of the items twice using different units for each measurement. Have them draw sketches of the items and record the measurements. Afterward, have a class discussion to compare answers and talk about strategies used in renaming.

18 inches
1 foot 6 inches
$\frac{1}{2}$ yard

Next, challenge students to convert some of the measurements they have just taken to different units.

- Convert a measurement from yards to inches.
- Convert a measurement from feet and inches to inches.
- Convert a measurement from feet to fractions of a yard.

Permit students to use calculators, but have them show their work on paper and make note of conversion strategies that prove helpful. Some students may benefit from a more concrete experience; encourage them to check their answers by actually measuring the items using the measurement units being converted to. The inconvenience of measuring a large object with a small unit like inches will also reinforce the importance of unit choice.

Discuss conversion methods briefly when students are finished. *How did you convert from yards to inches? What method did you use?* Highlight the fact that students may use several different methods to convert among linear units. In summarizing students' methods, point out that multiplication, division, addition, subtraction, and fraction operations are all useful for unit conversions.

CONCLUDE THE LESSON with a series of questions to reinforce the concept of unit sizes, the relationships among the units, and how the same measurement can be expressed in different ways. Encourage students to explain the thinking they use as they answer questions.

- *Is 46 inches closer to 3 feet or 4 feet?* (Closer to 4 feet, which equals 48 inches.)

- *How many feet are there in $4\frac{1}{3}$ yards?* (3 ft = 1 yd; 4 yd would be 12 ft; $\frac{1}{3}$ yd is 1 ft; 12 ft + 1 ft = 13 ft.)

- *A mile is 1,760 yards. About what fraction of a mile is 900 yards?* (About $\frac{1}{2}$ mile.)

- *How many inches are in 10 yards?* (36 in. = 1 yd; there are 360 inches in 10 yards.)

- *What fraction of a yard is 9 inches?* (36 in. = 1 yd; and $\frac{9}{36}$ in lowest terms is $\frac{1}{4}$; therefore, 9 in. = $\frac{1}{4}$ of a yard.)

Student Pages

Students should now be ready to complete exercises similar to those on the reduced student pages.

Assessment

As students chose appropriate units of measure, measured objects using different units of length, and renamed units using various conversion methods, it was possible to assess their understanding of the relationships among inches, feet, and yards. When students explained their choices and shared their reasoning by answering questions and explaining the strategies they used, it was possible to assess how well they grasped the lesson concepts.

NCTM Standards Summary

As students chose which units to use to measure various items, they focused on the lengths represented by those units. Measuring the same object first with one unit and then with another provided concrete representation of the relationship among the units and reinforced their connection to one another. Converting between units further reinforced connections among standard units and how they relate to mathematical operations and fractions. Class discussions on choosing appropriate measures and conversion methods allowed students to communicate their understanding of the relationships among inches, feet, yards, and miles.

Standard 5 **Data Analysis and Probability**

AT THE FIFTH GRADE LEVEL, data analysis and and probability include a lot of work with different graphical representations of data, statistical representations of a set of data, and probability concepts. Our lessons are derived from these important topics. They include a lesson on using the mean to compare sets of data, a lesson about choosing the best graph for representing a particular data set, a lesson that focuses on listing the possible outcomes in a sample space, and a lesson on creating a line graph.

Three lessons model how the process standards can be used to teach content. A fourth lesson is a hypothetical textbook lesson that we have revised to be more standards based. These four lessons do not represent the entire curriculum, but rather provide glimpses of how, with a more concentrated effort to incorporate the process standards, better mathematics teaching and learning can be achieved.

One lesson we have chosen focuses students on choosing and constructing an appropriate graph for a set of data. By basing this lesson on the process standards of communication, reasoning and proof, and representation, students try to make three different representations of the same data. They realize that it may not always be possible to represent the data using all three methods, and that one of the ways is preferable to the others.

Another lesson we have chosen has students comparing sets of data using the mean. By incorporating the process standards of representation, connections, and communication, students will gain a better sense of what the mean represents and how it compares to other statistical measures.

A third lesson we have chosen is one in which students use a tree diagram to list all of the possible outcomes of an event. By focusing on the process standards of problem solving, representation, and reasoning and proof, a lesson can be presented in which students must decide which options give them the best chance of winning a game. After a few trials, students will realize that an organized list of all of the options would be helpful.

The hypothetical textbook lesson we have chosen to revise is one in which students create and interpret information in a line graph. Through better incorporation of the process standards of representation, reasoning and proof, and communication, students are taught more about making a line graph. They also examine trends in the data in order to make predictions.

Standard 5 Lessons

Representing Data

Using Mean to Compare Data

Listing Possible Outcomes

Creating Line Graphs

Representing Data

Introduction

Objective → Students will be able to choose and construct an appropriate graphic representation for a given set of data.

Context → Students have had several experiences working with data as well as constructing and interpreting different types of graphs. They are ready to look critically at data sets and determine the best graphic representation for the data.

NCTM Standards Focus

Often students are presented with graphs already constructed and asked to interpret them. Rarely do students at this grade level discuss graphs as communication devices and decide what type of graph best communicates the information that needs to be presented. In this standards-based lesson, students will look at information they need to communicate and try to represent it in three different ways. By making three different types of graphs to display the same information, students will gain a better understanding of the advantages and disadvantages of the different representations of the same data.

Communication Communication is at the heart of this lesson. Students will understand that they are not just making a graph, but that they are using a graphic tool to communicate information.

Reasoning Students will use reasoning skills to determine what they believe to be the best type of graphic representation for a given set of data. They will construct a graph, present it to the class, and explain their reasons (in writing, as well as orally) for choosing to display the data as they did.

Representation Students will create three different representations of the same data. They will look at the different representations and analyze how effectively each representation conveys the given data. This lesson will let students begin to see that some representations do a better job of conveying information than do others.

Teaching Plan

Materials → Student pages 126–127; graph paper; unlined paper; optional materials for making graphs such as colored pencils; examples of bar graphs, pictographs, and line graphs

INTRODUCE THE LESSON by showing students examples of a pictograph, a bar graph and a line graph. Ask students to look at the graphs and to describe the information that each graph communicates. The following questions might help focus the discussion:

- *What is the purpose of the graph?*
- *What is the graph maker trying to tell you?*
- *Do you think he or she was successful? Why? Why not?*

- *Did any one thing stand out about the graph?*
- *Would a different type of graph do a better job of communicating the information?*

Focus the discussion on the types of graphs that students looked at. *Do you think this kind of graph is a good one for communicating the message? Why or why not?*

CONTINUE THE LESSON by organizing the class into groups of three. Groups of three work best since each group will make three graphs. Give each student graph paper and a copy of student page 126. Tell students that they should work each problem, making a pictograph, a bar graph, and a line graph to display the data given in the problems.

Students may find it difficult to construct a particular graph for certain situations, but they should try several ideas before giving up. Doing so will help them understand why some graphs may be better in some situations than others. The sunset and the food data present real challenges for making a pictograph. Because time is a continuous measure, it is a difficult measure to represent as an object. A possible solution might be to have one sun stand for each hour after noon. The lunch data is a bit more easily displayed in a pictograph. Students could have a picture of a lunch tray represent a certain number of meals. The important thing to remember is that not all data sets lend themselves to all kinds of graphs. The key goal of this lesson is to have students begin to recognize what kinds of graphs are best suited for representing a particular set of data.

As students work on their graphs ask them to identify the strengths and weaknesses of each kind of graph in terms of the information to be conveyed.

AS STUDENTS MAKE THEIR GRAPHS, circulate and ask them how the type of graph they are making suits the information they are trying to represent. When the groups are finished pull the class together for a discussion of what students discovered. *Do some types of graphs do a better job displaying certain kinds of data? Are there cases when it doesn't make sense to use a particular kind of graph? Are some kinds of data better shown on a particular kind of graph?* You may wish to use the same list of questions that were used to evaluate the graphs in the beginning of the lesson. While there are no definite answers to the questions, students need to back up their choices with solid reasoning.

f.y.i.

There are many things that people can do to enhance their points of view when making graphs. This lesson focuses on the types of graphs students may make; however some students may notice that they can manipulate the data within the type of graph to better show their points of view. Depending on the time you have, you may wish to discuss such issues without losing the focus of the lesson—that is, what type of graph best represents a particular data set.

Possible Student Responses

Problem 1

The sunset information might be best displayed in a line graph since the goal is to show change over time and the line graph will do that. A bar graph with bars close together will also show change over time.

Problem 2

The classroom information could be displayed in either a pictograph or a bar graph. But a pictograph could provide a visual that would attract attention in the newspaper.

Problem 3

The data from the cafeteria study may be best displayed in a bar graph since the goal is to compare information. A pictograph will probably give a less exact picture of the data since there will need to be partial units. The line graph probably does not add anything because there is no trend that is being looked at.

CONTINUE THE DISCUSSION leading students to make generalizations about the usefulness of the different kinds of graphs.

- *What kinds of data are best displayed in a pictograph? In a line graph, in a bar graph?*
- *Are there any cases when one kind of graph works as well as another?*
- *If so, why might you choose one over the other?*

If the following points are not brought out in the discussion, present them to the class for their consideration:

- A pictograph is often good for comparing data that is concrete and visual, such as hamburgers sold per day of the week.
- A bar graph is also good for comparing data. Since it uses bars it can focus on the scale of the difference between data points. A bar graph is also useful for conveying information that is not visual or concrete, such as the finish times of five different swimmers in a race.
- A line graph is useful for showing trends, such as the high temperatures for the week.

Student Pages

Student page 126 provides the three problems that students use in class. The problems provide the basis for discussion about the suitability of certain graphs for a particular set of data. Student page 127 gives students a situation and a set of data and asks them to make the appropriate graph and explain why their graph is the best one for displaying the given information.

Assessment

While students worked in groups, you observed them reason and select what they believed to be the best graphic representation of the given data. You assessed their ability to convey their reasoning when presenting to the whole class. You then observed how students could transfer this group experience into one where they were working on their own.

NCTM Standards Summary

In this lesson, students reasoned about how to convey information in the best format, deciding which type of graph would best communicate the given information. They constructed several different graphic representations of the same data and evaluated the results.

Answers

Page 126
Answers will vary. Suggested answers are given in the lesson.

Page 127
Answers may vary. Suggested answer: A line graph will do a good job of showing a trend towards the goal.

Representing Data

Solve the problems.

1 Mimi is doing a report on weather and the change of seasons. She wants to make a graph showing that the sun sets later each day as the days progress from January to June. She has the time of the sunset for the first day of each month.

All times are Central Standard Time	
January	4:30 p.m.
February	5:06 p.m.
March	5:43 p.m.
April	6:19 p.m.
May	6:53 p.m.
June	7:27 p.m.

2 A newspaper is doing an article on the size of schools in the local school district. The reporter wants to make a graph that shows the number of classes in each school. He believes that some of the schools are too large.

School A	28 classrooms
School B	18 classrooms
School C	25 classrooms
School D	12 classrooms
School E	30 classrooms

3 The school cafeteria manager is studying what lunches students like and buy. She needs to make decisions about how many lunches to make and what choices to offer. To begin her study she made a list of lunches sold last week. The manager wants to display the information in a graph.

Item	Lunches Sold
Pizza	65
Fish	24
Chicken	37
Spaghetti	49
Hamburgers	86

Standard 5 Data Analysis and Probability

Representing Data

**Make the graph you believe best communicates the information.
Explain your reasoning.**

1 You are going on a hiking vacation in the summer. Your goal is to work up to taking a 20-mile hike. Below are the distances you hiked on the last six Saturdays. Make a graph that would convince someone you will be ready to hike 20 miles within the next eight Saturdays.

Saturday	Miles Walked
1	3
2	5
3	5
4	7
5	9
6	10

Using Mean to Compare Data

Introduction

Objective → Students will compare sets of data by using the mean.

Context → Students have had some experience collecting and interpreting data. They are familiar with the concept of an average. After studying the mean, they will go on to learn about other measures of central tendency and spread, and will evaluate how well each measure represents a set of data.

NCTM Standards Focus

One of the goals of statistics is to summarize or describe a set of data using a single number. The concept of a representative or average value is commonly applied; mathematically, there are several ways to define the average of a set of data. Students need to learn how to choose the most appropriate measure for the particular set of data being studied. In this standards-based lesson, students work with real-world data that is relevant to them to explore the mean. They come to understand that this measure is found through a process of "evening out."

Representation Students represent data numerically and with manipulative materials. By using a model, they develop an understanding of the process for finding the mean of a data set.

Connections Students collect and organize data from real-world situations. They use prior knowledge about whole numbers and decimals to determine the mean and evaluate it as a measure of central tendency.

Communication Students work cooperatively, discussing methods for collecting, organizing, and analyzing the data they collect. They communicate their strategies and understandings both orally and in writing.

Teaching Plan

Materials → Student pages 132–133; counters or linking cubes; calculators (optional)

Preparation → Prior to beginning this lesson, ask students to record the number of hours they watch television for one complete weekend (Friday night through Sunday). When recording the number of hours for each day, students should estimate their viewing to the nearest hour. Let them know they will be using this data in a class activity.

BEGIN THE LESSON by distributing counters or linking cubes and present students with a situation to develop students' understanding of the process for finding the mean. *One morning, a group of students compared the number of books they each had brought to class. The numbers of books were 3, 6, 4, 8, and 4.*

Have students model this situation with their counters or cubes as you draw a diagram representing the number of each student's books on the board.

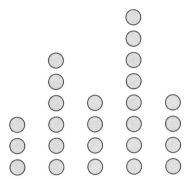

Ask students to copy the arrangement and then find a way to rearrange their cubes to show the same number of books for each student. When students have completed their work, encourage them to describe their methods.

Methods Students Might Use

- Moving items one by one from the columns that have more to those that have fewer until the columns are even.
- Combining all the counters or cubes to form one large group, then distributing or dividing the items into 5 equal groups.

By using some variation of these methods, students have tried to "be fair" or "even out" the numbers. Point out that by doing so, students were finding the *mean* of the set of books data. The mean represents an average of the data. The method of adding all the numbers of books together then dividing by the number of students illustrates the mathematical process for finding the mean.

HELP STUDENTS CLARIFY the procedure for finding the mean by asking questions that reinforce the thinking involved. *How many books were there all together?* (25) *How many students were there?* (5) *What did we say the mean was?* (5) *Did any student actually bring 5 books?* (No.) Emphasize that this shows the mean does not have to be one of the numbers in the data set. *How many students brought fewer than 5 books?* (3) *More than 5?* (2) *Is it reasonable to say students brought an average of 5 books to school?* (Answers may vary, but 5 is descriptive of this set of data.)

Remind students of the information they collected about TV viewing and tell them they are going to analyze their data. Have students form groups of five (or four when this is not possible). Groups of five will assure that decimal quotients will not exceed the tenths place.

DISTRIBUTE STUDENT PAGE 132. Instruct students to record each group member's name and complete the columns for daily and total viewing hours. Ask them to determine the average number of viewing hours for each day and for the entire weekend and have them record that information in the appropriate place in the table. You may wish to allow students to use a calculator to perform the calculations.

Instruct students to answer the questions at the bottom of the page after they have completed and checked their calculations. Tell them they are to decide on their answers as a group. These questions are designed to help students recognize certain features of the mean and to get them to think about how representative the mean values are of the entire data set. Opinions may vary among different groups, so students should be prepared to justify their conclusions.

CONCLUDE THE LESSON by having each group present its results. Create a chart on the board and record each group's daily and weekend average. Then ask questions that will help students interpret the information.

- *Are the values similar or very different among the groups?*
- *What conclusions can be drawn about TV viewing habits from the data?*
- *Within each group, were the individual values all close to the average value or were there some very high or very low values?*
- *Which groups felt that the overall mean for total weekend viewing was a good middle value? Why?*
- *Did any group feel that the mean did not represent their group fairly? Why?*
- *What is the relationship between the daily means and the overall mean?* (The overall mean should be the sum of the daily means. This provides a good method for checking work.)

Suppose the mean weekend viewing time for a group was 15 hours. Then, a new member who watched TV for 22 hours over the weekend joined the group. How would that change the mean for the whole group? Explain. (Since the new value is greater than the mean, the new mean will be greater.) Students may suggest that the extra hours above the mean will be divided among the members, raising the mean.

Extension

Present the frequency table of students' heights and have students find the mean of data displayed. Ask students to explain the method they use to calculate the mean. (Students may add each item repeatedly or multiply and then add.) The mean height is 63.4 inches.

Students' Heights in Inches

Height	62	63	64	65	66
Number of Students	5	3	4	2	1

Student Pages

Student page 132 provides recording space for the television viewing data and questions that prompt students to analyze their results. Student page 133 provides directions and recording space for a data activity involving names and also provides additional practice in comparing data sets using the mean.

Assessment

There were ample opportunities to assess students' understanding of the significance and process for finding the mean as they used manipulatives and as they worked in groups sharing and analyzing their television data. During class discussions it was possible to evaluate students' critical thinking and evaluate how they related the mean to the original data set. Explanations and answers to exercises on the student pages provide additional opportunities to assess students' proficiency with concepts and computational methods.

NCTM Standards Summary

In this lesson, students used a manipulative model to explore the concept of mean. They collected and displayed self-generated data and represented the set numerically. Students relied on prior knowledge of whole numbers, decimals, and operations as they calculated and interpreted the mean for different data sets. The situations in the lesson and on the student pages illustrated the connection of the mean to the real world. Throughout the lesson, students shared their ideas and communicated their understandings both orally and in writing.

Answers

Page 132
1–5. Answers may vary.

Page 133
1–2. Answers may vary.
3. Mrs. Curtis was wrong. The average for science classes is 35; the average for math is 33.8.
4. The mean is 47°F. Most temperatures were well below the mean. The two extreme values raised it.
5. The fourth student was 61 inches tall. $65 \times 4 = 260$, $62 + 67 + 70 = 199$, $260 - 199 = 61$

Using Mean to Compare Data

❶ Record the data for TV viewing this weekend for each member of your group. Determine the daily mean and total mean viewing times.

Mean of Time Spent Viewing TV in Hours

Group Member	Friday Night	Saturday	Sunday	Mean for Member
Group's Mean				

❷ How many members of your group had a total viewing time that was less than the mean? Greater than the mean?

❸ Did your data set have any very high or very low values? If so, explain how this affected the mean.

❹ Do you think the mean is a good way to represent the viewing habits of your group? Explain why or why not.

❺ Write a short summary about your investigation. Describe what you did and what you found out. Explain how the information you found could be useful to others.

Using Mean to Compare Data

Record name data for you and four of your friends. Write each person's first name, middle name, and last name in the appropriate column. After each name, write number of letters in the name. In the last column, write the total number of letters for the entire name. Then, find the mean for each column and record it in the bottom row of the column. Compare your results with classmates.

First name	Middle name	Last name	Total letters
Mean			

❶ In which column is the mean of the letters the highest? The lowest?

❷ Do you think the mean for total letters is representative of the names? Explain why or why not.

❸ Mrs. Curtis, the math teacher, thought that the average number of students in her classes was greater than the average number of students in Mr. Romero's science classes. Was she right? Explain.

Number of Students in Math Classes	Number of Students in Science Classes
36	37
34	35
42	34
27	35
30	34

❹ The daily high temperatures in Cooltown during a one-week period in March are shown. Find the mean temperature. Is the mean temperature representative? Explain.

Cooltown's Daily High Temperatures (°F)

Sun.	Mon.	Tues.	Wed.	Thur.	Fri.	Sat.
34°	36°	32°	33°	78°	76°	40°

❺ The average height of four students was 65 inches. The heights of three students were 62 inches, 67 inches, and 70 inches. What was the height of the fourth student? Explain how you found your answer.

Listing Possible Outcomes

Introduction

Objective → Students will use a tree diagram to list all possible outcomes of an event and will be able to determine whether a game is fair.

Context → Students have informally explored the concept of probability. They have worked with random samples to determine the makeup of a sample set. They will go on to use this lesson as a basis for understanding the counting principle.

NCTM Standards Focus

In this standards-based lesson, students will explore the concept of probability by engaging in a game and determining whether the game was fair. They will learn how to make and use tree diagrams as an organizational tool to determine the total number of possible outcomes for the game and the probability for each outcome to occur.

Representation Students will represent outcomes of events in tables and by making tree diagrams. They will organize information in ways to make it useful for predicting the probability of events.

Reasoning and Proof Students will apply reasoning skills as they analyze the data collected while playing a game and will make predictions regarding the fairness of the game. They will then use tree diagrams to check the accuracy of their predictions.

Connections Students will connect tree diagrams to probability. They see how this representation is useful in determining possible outcomes and the likelihood of events occurring.

Teaching Plan

Materials → Student pages 138–139; two-color counters

BEGIN THE LESSON by dividing the class into two groups. Assign each group one of the colors on your two-color counter, possibly red or yellow. Explain that you are going to flip a two-sided counter and that you will tally the color that lands "face up" for each flip. The team whose color reaches 10 tally marks first will be the winner. Ask students to think about whether or not this game is fair.

Play one game, recording the result of each flip on the board. Discuss students' assessment of the fairness of the game. Ask them to make a prediction about the outcome for playing the game a second time and to explain their reasoning. Then, play the game again and record each result. Have students compare their predictions with the actual results. Completing this exercise encourages students to connect the possible outcomes of each flip with the chances of winning the game.

Write the possible outcomes for flipping a two-color counter on the board. *What is the likelihood of the counter landing on red?* (There are two possible outcomes, one is red; the likelihood is 1 out of 2.) Explain that this likelihood can be expressed as a ratio in fraction form as $\frac{1}{2}$, or as a percentage as 50%. Students should now realize that the game is fair because there are two possible outcomes and each is equally likely.

Possible outcomes for flipping a 2-color counter

$$< {R \atop Y} \quad \frac{1}{2} \text{ or } 50\%$$

NOW TELL STUDENTS that this time you will flip the counter twice. One group will receive a point when both flips of the counter are the same color, and the other group will receive a point if the flip results in different colors. After ten flips, the team with more points will be the winner. Remind students to think about whether this new version of the game is fair.

Play this game once with the class. Before discussing whether this version of the game is fair, tell students that you would like them to gather more data.

DISTRIBUTE A COPY OF STUDENT PAGE 138 to each student. Have pairs of students play the two-flips game. After students have played several games, discuss their findings. Ask students to consider whether the game was fair or not and why they think so.

Remind students of the diagram showing the possible results for one flip of the counter. *How can this kind of diagram be used to show the result of two flips?* If students need help, point to the letter *R*, representing red, and guide them with questions. *Suppose the first flip turned up red. What could happen on the second flip?* Students should be able to explain that either another red or a yellow could occur. Demonstrate how to record this by extending the diagram. *How will you know when you have all the possible combinations?*

Possible outcomes for flipping a 2-color counter

First Flip   Second Flip

$$R < {R \atop Y}$$
$$Y$$

Explain that the diagram is called a *tree diagram. How many possible out-comes are there?* (4) List the outcomes. (R,R; R,Y; Y,R; Y,Y) *How can the tree diagram help us determine whether this is a fair game?* (It shows that there are two ways to get a red and yellow together, and two ways to get both colors the same. This is a fair game.)

What Might Happen . . . What to Do

One common misconception that students might have is that there are only three possible outcomes: R,R; R,Y; or Y,Y. Point out that while red/yellow and yellow/red each have one red and one yellow, they are two different occurrences.

Speculating about if they would receive an extra point if they flipped a red counter first and then a yellow, but lose a point if they flipped a yellow first and then a red, will make the distinction clear.

Ask students to draw a tree diagram to represent the results of three flips. Instruct them to make a list of all possible outcomes shown by their dia-grams. *How many possible outcomes are there?* (8) *How many outcomes are there for getting exactly two reds?* (3) *For getting three yellows?* (1)

First Second Third
Flip   Flip   Flip

R,R,R
R,R,Y
R,Y,R
R,Y,Y
Y,R,R
Y,R,Y
Y,Y,R
Y,Y,Y

Now let students play the game again, but with four flips of the counter, and with these rules:

- One player will get a point for any combination of two reds and two yellows that occur in their four flips.
- The other player will get a point for anything else.
- The first player to get ten points wins.

Instruct students that they are to play the game and see if this appears to be a fair game. Then have them make a tree diagram and list the possible outcomes. *How many possible outcomes are there?* (16) *How many outcomes are there for two reds and two yellows?* (6) *Is this a fair game?* (No.) *Why or why not?* (One player has only 6 ways to score a point whereas the other player has 10 ways.)

Student Pages

Student page 138 provides a chart for recording flips of the first game described in the lesson. Student page 139 has students make and interpret tree diagrams.

Assessment

When students discussed the games for flipping a two-color counter, there were opportunities to hear their thinking about the fairness of the game. As they completed tree diagrams and listed possible outcomes, it was possible to observe their understanding of this method for assessing fairness of a game.

NCTM Standards Summary

In this activity-based lesson, connections were made between information produced by tree diagrams and determining whether games are fair. Students collected, organized, and represented data in tables and made tree diagrams and lists of possible outcomes. They speculated on a game's fairness, and then they compared outcomes from a tree diagram with the results of actual play to support or alter their original thinking.

Answers

Page 138
Results will vary.

Page 139
1. 16
2. 4
3. 6
4. 1
5. Yes; each person has 8 outcomes that would score 1 point.
6. 27
7. 5
8. 8
9. No; Michael has 13 outcomes that score him 1 point whereas his friend has 14 outcomes that score 1 point.

Listing Possible Outcomes

Play the game. Flip a two-color counter and record your results in the table.
Flip the counter a second time and record the result.
Then, write the results of both flips in the order they occurred.

Turn	Flip #1	Flip #2	Results for Two Flips
1			
2			
3			
4			
5			
6			
7			
8			
9			
10			

Turn	Flip #1	Flip #2	Results for Two Flips
1			
2			
3			
4			
5			
6			
7			
8			
9			
10			

Turn	Flip #1	Flip #2	Results for Two Flips
1			
2			
3			
4			
5			
6			
7			
8			
9			
10			

Turn	Flip #1	Flip #2	Results for Two Flips
1			
2			
3			
4			
5			
6			
7			
8			
9			
10			

Standard 5 Data Analysis and Probability

Name _____

Listing Possible Outcomes

Jenny tosses a coin four times in a row.
You can make a tree diagram to help answer the questions.

1 How many possible outcomes are there?

2 How many outcomes have 3 heads and 1 tail?

3 How many outcomes have 2 heads and 2 tails?

4 How many outcomes have 4 tails?

5 Jenny devises a game in which she gets 1 point for the outcomes with 2 heads and 2 tails or with all four tosses the same. Her friend gets 1 point for all outcomes of 3 heads or tails and 1 tail or head. Is this game fair? Explain.

Michael spins the spinner three times in a row.
You can make a tree diagram to help answer the questions.

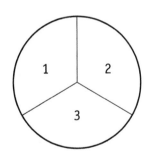

6 How many possible outcomes are there?

7 How many outcomes have two 3s?

8 How many outcomes do not have any 1s?

9 Michael devises a game in which he gets 1 point for an outcome that has a sum of 5 or 6. His friend gets 1 point for any other outcome. Is this game fair? Explain.

Creating Line Graphs

Introduction

Objective → Students will interpret and then create line graphs.

Context → This lesson is near the end of a study of data that has included measures of central tendency and reading and creating different types of graphs. Students have had experience with graphing on the coordinate plane.

Creating Line Graphs

Learn

You will need grid paper and a ruler.
Chantelle's mother owns a sandwich shop. She records the number of sandwiches sold at the end of each hour. (57 sandwiches were sold from 10 to 11 a.m.)

Sandwich Shop Sales					
Hour	**11 a.m.**	**12 noon**	**1 p.m.**	**2 p.m.**	**3 p.m.**
Sandwiches	57	70	89	65	39

You can make a line graph to see the changes in the number of sandwiches sold.

Working Together

1. Use grid paper.
   a. Title the graph and draw the axes.
   b. Find the range and choose a scale for the vertical axis.
   c. Put the hours on the horizontal axis.
   d. Place a point on the graph for each ordered pair.
   e. Connect the points using line segments.

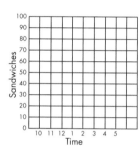

Remember To find the ordered pair (1, 4), you move 1 to the right on the horizontal axis and move up 4 on the vertical axis.

2. About how many sandwiches might be sold at the Sandwich Shop by 1:30?

3. Explain how your line graph helped you find the number of sandwiches sold at the sandwich shop at 1:30?

NCTM Process Standards Analysis and Focus

The standards analysis examines how the process standards have been incorporated into the above lesson. By increasing the focus on three of the process standards, a more effective and meaningful lesson can be presented. The suggestions offered can help you to think about how this might be accomplished.

Representation The lesson gives directions for representing information in a line graph but does not include instructions about organizing labeling information. The completed grid is presented.

Suggestion → Increase attention to the way information is represented and what that information means. Have students consider the title and labeling information along the axes. Discuss

Try

You can also use line graphs to help you see trends. Trends are changes in data over time.

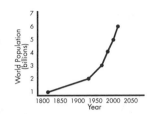

You can see that the earth's population has increased greatly over time. For example, the population in 2050 would be much greater than 6 billion.

Practice

1. Use the information in this table to make a line graph.

Average Monthly Rainfall in Mudville

Month	Jan.	Feb.	Mar.	April	May	June	July	Aug.	Sept.	Oct.	Nov.	Dec.
Rain in cm.	22	15	13	10	8	7	2	4	9	12	23	25

2. Use your graph to determine the months Mudville has the greatest amount of rain.

3. Between which months is there the greatest increase in the average rainfall? The greatest decrease?

4. Science: When the wind blows the temperature feels colder than it actually is. This is called wind chill. The greater the speed of the wind, the colder it feels. The data below shows what the temperature would feel like on a 35 degree day at different wind speeds. Make a graph that shows what the different wind speeds would make the temperature feel like.

Wind Speed (mph)	5	10	15	20	25	30
Wind Chill	33	22	16	12	8	6

5. Can you explain how a line graph might be used to make predictions?

whether the graph shows trends by determining whether the line moves steadily in an upward or downward direction. This will allow students to understand general and specific information as they interpret and create line graphs.

Reasoning and Proof The lesson indicates that estimations and predictions can be made by using information on line graphs and asks students to do so.

Suggestion → Have students identify trends in line graphs and use those trends to interpret information and to make predictions. These activities will help them to develop critical thinking skills as they work with graphs.

Communication Opportunities for communication are limited to answering direct questions and explaining how the graph was helpful in answering those questions.

Suggestion → An increased focus on reasoning and representation will open up opportunities to talk about how information is organized. This will result in a stronger understanding of how to read and create these graphs.

Problem Solving Although reasoning is involved in interpreting and creating graphs, problem solving is not incorporated into this lesson.

Connections A nice connection is made between a line graph containing scientific data and making predictions based on the information presented, however, applications for the information found are not mentioned.

The teaching plan that follows shows how the suggestions for increasing the focus on the process standards can implemented.

Revised Teaching Plan

Materials → Overhead transparencies of Figures A, B, and C, prepared prior to the lesson; grid or graph paper; straightedge

Preparation → Prior to presenting the lesson, either make copies of the table entitled "Visitors to the Aquarium During 1999" found on page 144 to distribute to students, or copy data onto the board or chart paper.

BEGIN THE LESSON by displaying Figure A. Pose questions to help students focus on the information represented in the graph. *What does this graph represent? Explain how you know.* (The graph represents sales of Slurp cereal. The title tells what the graph is about.) Direct students to look at the information along the axes of the graph. *What do the numbers along the bottom, or horizontal axis, of the graph represent?* (The years 1994 through 1999.) *What do the numbers along the side, or vertical axis, of the graph represent?* (The number of boxes sold.) *What is the greatest number of boxes of cereal that could be shown on this graph? Explain.* (90 million boxes. The numbers along the vertical axis represent boxes in the millions.)

Before asking students specific details about the graph, encourage them to communicate their general impressions of the information represented. *Have sales increased or decreased during the period of time shown on the graph?* (Increased) *How do you know?* (The line starts lower and keeps going up.) *If the graph were continued to show sales for the next year, what would you expect it to show?* (An increase) *Why?* (Since sales have increased each year, it would make sense to think that they would continue to do so.)

Explain that when the overall direction of the line shows an increase, the graph is said to show an *upward trend.* If the overall direction shows a decrease, the graph is said to show a *downward trend. What kind of trend does the graph of cereal sales show?* (An upward trend) This line of questioning draws attention to the feature for which line graphs are most popular—showing trends over time.

Sales of Slurp Cereal
(in millions)

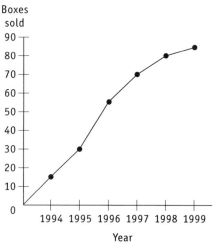

Figure A

Now, make sure students know how to read the graph for specific information. *How many boxes of cereal were sold in 1995?* (30 million boxes) *Between which two years is the greatest increase in sales shown?* (Between 1995 and 1996) *The smallest increase?* (Between 1998 and 1999)

DISPLAY FIGURES B AND C on the overhead projector and invite students to share their general impressions of the two graphs. *How would you describe the trend in Figure B? How do you know?* (Following a steep rise, the graph shows a downward trend. After a peak in sales in 1995, the number of computer systems sold declines steadily to a low in 1999.) *If this graph continued, what might you expect?* (Students may say that the graph would continue to show a decline in sales or it might level off.) *What does the data in Figure C tell you about the number of CD-ROMs sold during the year?* (The number sold during each of the 4 quarters was close—within a 1,000 CD-ROMs. There was neither an upward nor a downward trend in sales.) Then ask students to generalize about the value and use of the data represented in each graph. *Who might be interested in the sales performance of Lemon Computer Systems?* (Company executives, industry analysts, stockholders, competing companies, and so on) *Who might be interested in the data in Figure C?* (Head of the company, sales/marketing director, potential customers, retail companies, and possible investors in the company) Point out that line graphs are excellent tools for displaying data that can change over time.

Distribute grid paper and the prepared data about visitors to the aquarium (see the following page). Tell students that they will create their own line graphs from data in a table.

BEGIN MODELING HOW TO CREATE a line graph from the set of data. Demonstrate how to draw the axis lines, pointing out that students need to leave room for labeling. Next, label each axis. Begin by indicating the months along the horizontal axis. Point out that abbreviations for the names of the months should be evenly spaced so that the graph will be easy to read. *There are twelve months, and so we need to make the axis long enough.* Show students how to make marks along the axis line to indicate which line of the graph represents each month. Then show the class how to label the vertical axis. Emphasize using numbers in equal intervals and spacing them equally along the axis. Remind students to make marks along

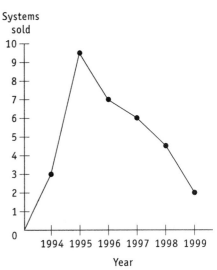

Sales of Lemon Computer Systems (in millions)

Figure B

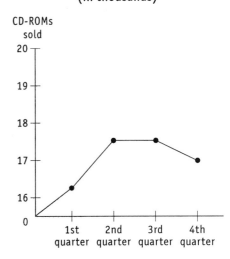

Sales of CD-ROMS at EZ Software, Inc. (in thousands)

Figure C

Visitors to the Aquarium During 1999 (in thousands)	
Month	Number of Visitors*
January	4
February	5
March	6
April	7
May	8
June	9
July	12
August	14
September	10
October	8
November	7
December	9

*Numbers rounded to the nearest thousand.

the axis to indicate the position of the numbers. *What numbers should I use for this axis?* (Numbers from 0 to 14, or even numbers from 0 to 14) *How should I label this axis?* ("Number of Visitors"—same as in table)

As you demonstrate how to place this labeling information, have students replicate your model to create graphs of their own. Circulate and observe students as they work to make sure they are placing information correctly. Catching errors early will help prevent students from having to redo their entire graph because of mislabeling. Only after the axes are clearly labeled and evenly marked should the data be entered.

Next, model how to plot the data points. *The table shows that about 4,000 visitors came to the aquarium in January. That means on the graph I should place the first point at the place where January and 4,000 intersect, directly above Jan. and directly across from 4 on the vertical axis.* Plot the data for the next few months, and then ask students to plot all the points on their own line graphs. Again, move around the class and offer assistance as needed.

FINALLY, HAVE STUDENTS USE a straightedge to connect the data points. Explain that this is done to help see increases and decreases and determine trends more easily. Be sure to have students write a title for their graphs. *What would be a good title for this graph?* [Visitors to the Aquarium During 1999 (in thousands)]

Instruct students to spend a few moments studying their line graphs. Then ask questions to determine whether students can interpret the data correctly. *What trend(s) does the graph reveal about the number visitors to the aquarium?* (The number of visitors is higher during the summer months when families are on vacation. A slight increase also occurs during the December holiday season.) *Do you think that this trend is likely to occur in subsequent years? Explain.* (Yes, so long as families continue to take vacations during the summer months.) *Who might be interested in the information in this graph?* (Aquarium officials, veterinarians, curators of special exhibits, vendors at the aquarium, tour business operators, and families planning visits, etc.)

CONCLUDE THE LESSON by asking students to write several questions of their own about the line graph they constructed. Then invite individual students to present their questions to the class for answering or discussion. To summarize the lesson, ask students to share their thoughts about using the tabular data to create a line graph. If no one suggests it, point out that the while table and the graph contain the same information, the advantage of the graph is that it gives the reader a visual representation of the data and makes it easier to analyze any apparent trends and make predictions.

Student Pages

Students should now be ready to complete exercises similar to those on the reduced student pages.

Assessment

Ample opportunities for assessing students' ability to interpret data in a line graph were built into the lesson. By answering specific questions about the format and the data presented in these graphs, students were able to demonstrate their understanding of trends and apparent changes in data over time. Students also created their own line graphs and answered questions about the data represented.

NCTM Standards Summary

Students learned firsthand why line graphs are ideal tools for representing data that can change over time. By studying how data is represented in line graphs, students were better prepared to analyze the information, describe trends, and use the data to make predictions. Students applied reasoning as they interpreted trends and made predictions, thus gaining additional experience in using critical thinking skills to analyze data. Throughout the lesson, students engaged in discussions that allowed them to communicate their ideas and share insights about line graphs in general and offer their interpretations of the represented data.

Create Your Own Lesson

THIS LAST CHAPTER IS DESIGNED TO HELP you develop your own lessons in which you can comfortably incorporate the NCTM standards with your teaching style. We start with a list of questions to help you focus on factors to consider as you begin to organize a standards-based lesson. Then, we model the process used to create a lesson, as you are walked through the thoughts and decisions one person used in developing a lesson.

The questions listed here are meant as a guide, a starting point; they are offered to get you thinking about how to develop your lesson, what material to cover, what steps to follow, what questions to ask. Hopefully, these questions will trigger additional ideas that you will add as you go along.

Write down the ideas that come to you as you read each question. There may be questions for which you don't have an immediate response, but don't worry; as you begin working on your lesson, ideas will come. Start by selecting the general content area. Think about the concept you want to develop. Then, narrow in on an objective for the lesson. Be specific and be realistic. What does meeting that objective mean? Is there a skill that students should be able to perform after completing the lesson? Are there questions they should be able to answer? How will you determine that the objective has been met?

Next, think about the process standards: Problem Solving, Reasoning and Proof, Communication, Connections, and Representation. What approach will be effective in helping students understand the concept? Try to envision how the lesson will flow, how it should begin, what activities and questions will be included, and how you will assess learning. Understand that there can be several ways to successfully teach any lesson. As you begin to design your lesson, new ideas will come and you will be able to refine your thinking.

Focusing Questions

1. What content standard is to be addressed? What concept within that standard is to be developed?

2. What information do the standards offer about this content?

3. What do students know about this content? What don't they know?

4. What is the specific objective of the lesson? What should students be able to do at the end of the lesson?

recognize	identify	define
review	compute	classify
compare	create	other

5. What kinds of questions should students be able to answer when they complete this lesson? What skill(s) should they be able to demonstrate?

6. What resources are available to develop this concept?

references	textual material
manipulatives	supplementary material
colleagues	student knowledge

7. What can realistically be accomplished in the time allowed?

8. Which activities and process standards can best help develop the key ideas?
    - using drawings, charts, diagrams (Representation)
    - focusing on symbols (Representation)
    - conducting small-group/large-group discussion (Communication)
    - having students gather and analyze data (Problem Solving)
    - thinking through relationships and explaining them (Reasoning and Proof and Communication)
    - finding ways to prove thinking and verify solutions (Reasoning and Proof)
    - extending/building on former knowledge (Connections)
    - integrating the concept with another discipline (Connections)
    - relating math to its use in the real world (Connections)

9. What questions will focus students' thinking on the concept and help guide learning?

Developing the Lesson

MY GOAL IS TO CREATE A LESSON that helps my students understand how to find the area of a triangle. This is part of the measurement standard. Most math materials I've looked at tend to show students exactly how to find the area, and then ask students to determine the areas of various triangles. The emphasis, it seems, is on memorization. When I think about the standards' emphasis on thinking, problem solving, and depth of understanding, I think it would be helpful to my students if I could design a lesson that really helps them build a solid conceptual understanding of the area of a triangle.

As I think more about how to develop such a lesson, I wonder about the approach to take. Fortunately, the standards give some guidance on this, as they suggest that the students themselves determine the formula for the area of a triangle. I can imagine that this lesson could be made challenging, by providing some initial discovery and discussion about the concept. It seems to me that a lesson on the area of a triangle must certainly include an activity that asks students to see if they can figure out a rule to determine the area of a triangle. I know that some of the students in my class may have been exposed to the formula. I don't want students just to find a rule. I want them to convince the rest of the class that their rule makes sense and will work in all cases.

We are just starting to look at the area of a rectangle. I know they have worked with it before. They know the formula and can find the area by counting squares on grid paper. Since many students can understand the area of triangles by working with rectangles, I will work with triangles right after we are finished with rectangles.

This will be a good lesson for reasoning and proof to play a key role in. Some students, I think, will want to show their idea, one example of how it works, and say they have the rule. But I want to make sure they convince the class. I want to make sure they can show that the rule will work for all different kinds of triangles. As I think about this, it will be important to look at the triangles that I use in the beginning of the lesson. I know my students can get frustrated when they don't get the answer right away. I have been working with them to see that, frequently, it takes hard work to understand something new. But I need to use my knowledge about triangles to let students get some insights and then bring in more complicated situations to test their insights.

There are some other concerns I have about hands-on work with triangles. I don't want the measurements to get in the way of the understanding. This is not really a lesson about calculating different areas of triangles. It is a lesson about understanding how to find the area of a triangle and how a rule works. Not only will I need to keep the measurements simple, I will need to have a method for the class to determine the approximate area just by looking at the triangle. Because of this, it seems essential that we work on grid paper. The representations of the triangles are important, and it is important that we all understand what the representations mean. Therefore, grid paper seems to be necessary so we can use representations that will communicate to all of us. Using grid paper will make it easier for students to explain their methods and convince us that they are correct.

An outline for the lesson is beginning to take shape. I will ask students only to work with right triangles in the beginning. This will make it easier for them to find the height of the triangles and to see the connection between triangles and rectangles. Also, it will make it easier for them to find the area using the grids. When I develop a lesson like this, I need to think about what information will help them reason to find a rule. Often, I just think they will get it, but they need to have information to get it. The first thing that may help some of them come up with their rules, is the relationship between triangles and rectangles. In this case, they will be able to put the two right triangles together to form a rectangle. The second is to look at the relationship between the sides and the areas of triangles.

Not only will it be important to give them some initial triangles to work with, it will also be helpful to give them suggestions before they start, about what data to look for, such as side measurements, or to have this information come out in a discussion. After we have our initial discussion, I will send them off to work with a partner to try to find a rule. Then, we will come back together to discuss what they found out. This will give students the chance to benefit from each other's thinking. After students have shown their ideas, I will ask them if they can use their rule with another type of triangle Now, I will show them some non-right triangles. We will discuss the difference between these triangles. They will go back with their partners and see if their ideas work or if they have to make modifications. I hope we can get this accomplished in a day. If we cannot, I think I will break the lesson after our discussion of the results of their work with right triangles.

NOW I NEED TO PLAN THE DETAILS of my lesson. To start the lesson, I will tell the students that their goal is to develop a rule for determining the area of the triangles that are on the sheet of centimeter grid paper that I will be giving them. As I said before, I want to stay with right triangles to make it easier for students to see the connection to rectangles and that the height and one of the sides will be the same. I am going to give them a 3-4-5 right triangle. Also, I want to give them an isosceles right triangle with sides 4, 4, and 5, 6. Finally, I will give them another 3-4-5 right triangle with sides measuring 6, 8, and 10. I am not going to limit them to these triangles, but these triangles are fairly easy to work with. As I said earlier, I don't want the measurement issue to throw off the lesson. That is one reason I am working in centimeters. I think it will be easier for the students to measure the sides. This also reminds me that we should talk, for a minute, about the fact that measurement is not exact. I will tell students that they should be as accurate as they can be. However, they should account for small inaccuracies when looking at relationships between sides and areas.

There are two more things I want to make sure students understand before they go off on their own. I want to do a quick review of finding the area by counting the squares. I mainly want to go over dealing with parts of squares. These first triangles will be relatively easy, but others could get more complex. Again, I want students to see that their measurements are approximations. Second, I want to talk to students about information they may want to record to see if there are patterns. If sides are not mentioned as important in our discussion, I will ask about how to find the area of a rectangle, hoping that will spark a connection. Also, I will ask students how they will note which sides they are recording. That will be an important part of this lesson, since one of these sides is also the height. I will remind the students that they need to find the areas for the triangles that I showed them, but they can also make some of their own. They may want to make them all right triangles like the ones I made for the first part of the lesson.

Then I will have the students work with their partners. I will go around the room and see how students are doing. As they record their information, I will reinforce the fact that they need some notation for remembering which side they recorded. Also, I will reinforce that they need to look for relationships. Finally, I will look for pairs of students who see that these triangles are half a rectangle and encourage their thinking in this direction.

When I think that at least some pairs have some rules to discuss, I will bring the class back together for a discussion on what they've found. This communication is important. I want to make sure that students who aren't quite there yet, hear ideas from other students rather than from me. I believe they will look more critically at some of the students' ideas and try to determine if they are true; often, they accept my ideas without thinking about them.

During this discussion, I want students to try to convince us that their rules work. In order to encourage my students to be the ones to challenge other students, I will need to model this behavior. I want students to understand that when I challenge them it doesn't mean they are necessarily wrong, it means they have to show their thinking. I am very interested in what the students have come up with. I should have some idea about what to expect, since I circulated around the room while they were working.

There are several points that I want to discover. These points will help in the next part of the lesson. First, I want students to focus again on the fact that they were working with right triangles. Also, when some students see that there is a pattern—that the area is half the product of two sides—I want to make sure they see that the sides make up the right angle. Also, I want students to see that the area of the triangle is half the area of the rectangle created out of two triangles. These points are important for working with non-right triangles. I am pretty sure that some of my students will come up with these ideas. If they don't, I will suggest them and have the class discuss them. Before I start explaining the next task, I want to review the suggested rules different members of the class have discovered. I will put them on the board so they can be referred to during the rest of lesson.

NEXT, I WILL SHOW STUDENTS an overhead of some non-right triangles drawn on graph paper. If we are running short of time, I will save this part for the next day. I will ask students how they could make a right angle in any of these triangles. We will take a minute to discuss this and see how a line can be dropped to the base, or even outside of, the triangle. I will suggest to students that they may want to record the measure of this line along with the sides. Then, I will have students look at these triangles and see if their rules still apply.

When I made the triangles for the second part of the activity, I also made them in a special way to make them easier for the students to work with and see if there rules worked. The new triangles I made had a whole number of centimeters for the base and for the height. However, I did not draw the height line. An example is below.

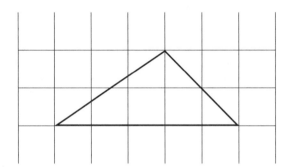

Again, I will circulate among students as they work in pairs. I want to focus on making sure they take the measure for the height of the triangle along with the sides. I also want to see if anyone is trying to make this triangle into a rectangle. Since this is complicated, I am ready to give suggestions to any pair that is trying.

I will call the pairs back together and ask them to share their results. One change that we should see is that students will need to add the concept of height to the rule. In the first triangles they worked with, the height was one of the sides. In these, they had to create the height. This will require some time to write the rule so it makes sense. I am not that concerned that we write the rule like the formula. In fact, I would like to use more informal language. This way I can be a little surer of what students are communicating and that they understand what they are saying. Finally, if no one shows how to turn this type of triangle into a rectangle, I will do it. This will help students visualize why the area of this triangle is half the base times the height.

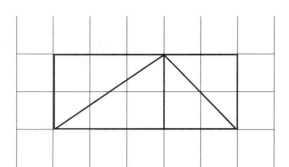

As I look back on this lesson, I think there are a lot of details that are impor-tant. The students are going to do a lot of reasoning, but there are some things I need to do to help them along. The triangles I make are important. It is important that I lead the discussions, so there is information to help the students think. I am convinced they can gain some understanding, but I need to look for opportunities to get them to think about what is important.

How can you prove your rule works? Here is an opportunity for the students to use reasoning and proof. Students will have the chance to challenge each other's rules and proofs at this time. I can help this along by asking things like: *Can someone give a new triangle's dimensions so we can see if this rule works for other triangles?*

Once all the pairs have presented, and hopefully reflected on what they've seen from their classmates, I will give the students an opportunity to refine their rules. *Given what you've seen and heard, how do you feel about your rule now? Should it be adjusted or changed in some way?* I will have volunteer groups share their adjusted rules.

Reviewing the Plan

Before I teach this lesson, I'll make sure it has all the components it needs to be successful. Specifically, I will look again at my use of the process stan-dards, knowing full well how much these enhance student learning. I believe the lesson will be effective because the students will do so much of their own thinking and investigating before the actual area formula is presented. The lesson has problem solving, opportunities to represent mathematical ideas, and plenty of instances of students communicating their mathematical thinking. In the end, I think this lesson will work far better than the cursory treatments given in most textbooks.